Science 100
Teacher's Guide Part 2

CONTENTS

Author: **Phyllis A. MacDonald, M.Ed.**
Revision Editor: Alan Christopherson, M.S.

Alpha Omega Publications®

804 N. 2nd Ave. E., Rock Rapids, IA 51246-1759

OVERVIEW

SCIENCE

Curriculum Overview
Grades 1–12

Science LIFEPAC Overview

	Grade 1	Grade 2	Grade 3
LIFEPAC 1	YOU LEARN WITH YOUR EYES • Name and group some colors • Name and group some shapes • Name and group some sizes • Help from what you see	THE LIVING AND NONLIVING • What God created • Rock and seed experiment • God-made objects • Man-made objects	YOU GROW AND CHANGE • Air we breathe • Food for the body • Exercise and rest • You are different
LIFEPAC 2	YOU LEARN WITH YOUR EARS • Sounds of nature and people • How sound moves • Sound with your voice • You make music	PLANTS • How are plants alike • Habitats of plants • Growth of plants • What plants need	PLANTS • Plant parts • Plant growth • Seeds and bulbs • Stems and roots
LIFEPAC 3	MORE ABOUT YOUR SENSES • Sense of smell • Sense of taste • Sense of touch • Learning with my senses	ANIMALS • How are animals alike • How are animals different • What animals need • Noah and the ark	ANIMAL GROWTH AND CHANGE • The environment changes • Animals are different • How animals grow • How animals change
LIFEPAC 4	ANIMALS • What animals eat • Animals for food • Animals for work • Pets to care for	YOU • How are people alike • How are you different • Your family • Your health	YOU ARE WHAT YOU EAT • Food helps your body • Junk foods • Food groups • Good health habits
LIFEPAC 5	PLANTS • Big and small plants • Special plants • Plants for food • House plants	PET AND PLANT CARE • Learning about pets • Caring for pets • Learning about plants • Caring for plants	PROPERTIES OF MATTER • Robert Boyle • States of matter • Physical changes • Chemical changes
LIFEPAC 6	GROWING UP HEALTHY • How plants and animals grow • How your body grows • Eating and sleeping • Exercising	YOUR FIVE SENSES • Your eye • You can smell and hear • Your taste • You can feel	SOUNDS AND YOU • Making sounds • Different sounds • How sounds move • How sounds are heard
LIFEPAC 7	GOD'S BEAUTIFUL WORLD • Types of land • Water places • The weather • Seasons	PHYSICAL PROPERTIES • Colors • Shapes • Sizes • How things feel	TIMES AND SEASONS • The earth rotates • The earth revolves • Time changes • Seasons change
LIFEPAC 8	ALL ABOUT ENERGY • God gives energy • We use energy • Ways to make energy • Ways to save energy	OUR NEIGHBORHOOD • Things not living • Things living • Harm to our world • Caring for our world	ROCKS AND THEIR CHANGES • Forming rocks • Changing rocks • Rocks for buildings • Rock collecting
LIFEPAC 9	MACHINES AROUND YOU • Simple levers • Simple wheels • Inclined planes • Using machines	CHANGES IN OUR WORLD • Seasons • Change in plants • God's love never changes • God's Word never changes	HEAT ENERGY • Sources of heat • Heat energy • Moving heat • Benefits and problems of heat
LIFEPAC 10	WONDERFUL WORLD OF SCIENCE • Using your senses • Using your mind • You love yourself • You love the world	LOOKING AT OUR WORLD • Living things • Nonliving things • Caring for our world • Caring for ourselves	PHYSICAL CHANGES • Change in man • Change in plants • Matter and time • Sound and energy

Grade 4	Grade 5	Grade 6	
PLANTS • Plants and living things • Using plants • Parts of plants • The function of plants	CELLS • Cell composition • Plant and animal cells • Life of cells • Growth of cells	PLANT SYSTEMS • Parts of a plant • Systems of photosynthesis • Transport systems • Regulatory systems	LIFEPAC 1
ANIMALS • Animal structures • Animal behavior • Animal instincts • Man protects animals	PLANTS: LIFE CYCLES • Seed producing plants • Spore producing plants • One-celled plants • Classifying plants	ANIMAL SYSTEMS • Digestive system • Excretory system • Skeletal system • Diseases	LIFEPAC 2
MAN'S ENVIRONMENT • Resources • Balance in nature • Communities • Conservation and preservation	ANIMALS: LIFE CYCLES • Invertebrates • Vertebrates • Classifying animals • Relating function and structure	PLANT AND ANIMAL BEHAVIOR • Animal behavior • Plant behavior • Plant-animal interaction • Balance in nature	LIFEPAC 3
MACHINES • Work and energy • Simple machines • Simple machines together • Complex machines	BALANCE IN NATURE • Needs of life • Dependence on others • Prairie life • Stewardship of nature	MOLECULAR GENETICS • Reproduction • Inheritance • DNA and mutations • Mendel's work	LIFEPAC 4
ELECTRICITY AND MAGNETISM • Electric current • Electric circuits • Magnetic materials • Electricity and magnets	TRANSFORMATION OF ENERGY • Work and energy • Heat energy • Chemical energy • Energy sources	CHEMICAL STRUCTURE • Nature of matter • Periodic Table • Diagrams of atoms • Acids and bases	LIFEPAC 5
PROPERTIES OF MATTER • Properties of water • Properties of matter • Molecules and atoms • Elements	RECORDS IN ROCK: THE FLOOD • The Biblical account • Before the flood • The flood • After the flood	LIGHT AND SOUND • Sound waves • Light waves • The visible spectrum • Colors	LIFEPAC 6
WEATHER • Causes of weather • Forces of weather • Observing weather • Weather instruments	RECORDS IN ROCK: FOSSILS • Fossil types • Fossil location • Identifying fossils • Reading fossils	MOTION AND ITS MEASUREMENT • Definition of force • Rate of doing work • Laws of motion • Change in motion	LIFEPAC 7
THE SOLAR SYSTEM • Our solar system • The big universe • Sun and planets • Stars and space	RECORDS IN ROCK: GEOLOGY • Features of the earth • Rock of the earth • Forces of the earth • Changes in the earth	SPACESHIP EARTH • Shape of the earth • Rotation and revolution • Eclipses • The solar system	LIFEPAC 8
THE PLANET EARTH • The atmosphere • The hydrosphere • The lithosphere • Rotation and revolution	CYCLES IN NATURE • Properties of matter • Changes in matter • Natural cycles • God's order	ASTRONOMY AND THE STARS • History of astronomy • Investigating stars • Major stars • Constellations	LIFEPAC 9
GOD'S CREATION • Earth and solar system • Matter and weather • Using nature • Conservation	LOOK AHEAD • Plant and animal life • Balance in nature • Biblical records • Records of rock	THE EARTH AND THE UNIVERSE • Plant systems • Animal systems • Physics and chemistry • The earth and stars	LIFEPAC 10

Science LIFEPAC Overview

	Grade 7	Grade 8	Grade 9
LIFEPAC 1	**WHAT IS SCIENCE** • Tools of a scientist • Methods of a scientist • Work of a scientist • Careers in science	**SCIENCE AND SOCIETY** • Definition of science • History of science • Science today • Science tomorrow	**OUR ATOMIC WORLD** • Structure of matter • Radioactivity • Atomic nuclei • Nuclear energy
LIFEPAC 2	**PERCEIVING THINGS** • History of the metric system • Metric units • Advantages of the metric system • Graphing data	**STRUCTURE OF MATTER I** • Properties of matter • Chemical properties of matter • Atoms and molecules • Elements, compounds, & mixtures	**VOLUME, MASS, AND DENSITY** • Measure of matter • Volume • Mass • Density
LIFEPAC 3	**EARTH IN SPACE I** • Ancient stargazing • Geocentric Theory • Copernicus • Tools of astronomy	**STRUCTURE OF MATTER II** • Changes in matter • Acids • Bases • Salts	**PHYSICAL GEOLOGY** • Earth structures • Weathering and erosion • Sedimentation • Earth movements
LIFEPAC 4	**EARTH IN SPACE II** • Solar energy • Planets of the sun • The moon • Eclipses	**HEALTH AND NUTRITION** • Foods and digestion • Diet • Nutritional diseases • Hygiene	**HISTORICAL GEOLOGY** • Sedimentary rock • Fossils • Crustal changes • Measuring time
LIFEPAC 5	**THE ATMOSPHERE** • Layers of the atmosphere • Solar effects • Natural cycles • Protecting the atmosphere	**ENERGY I** • Kinetic and potential energy • Other forms of energy • Energy conversions • Entropy	**BODY HEALTH I** • Microorganisms • Bacterial infections • Viral infections • Other infections
LIFEPAC 6	**WEATHER** • Elements of weather • Air masses and clouds • Fronts and storms • Weather forecasting	**ENERGY II** • Magnetism • Current and static electricity • Using electricity • Energy sources	**BODY HEALTH II** • Body defense mechanisms • Treating disease • Preventing disease • Community health
LIFEPAC 7	**CLIMATE** • Climate and weather • Worldwide climate • Regional climate • Local climate	**MACHINES I** • Measuring distance • Force • Laws of Newton • Work	**ASTRONOMY** • Extent of the universe • Constellations • Telescopes • Space explorations
LIFEPAC 8	**HUMAN ANATOMY I** • Cell structure and function • Skeletal and muscle systems • Skin • Nervous system	**MACHINES II** • Friction • Levers • Wheels and axles • Inclined planes	**OCEANOGRAPHY** • History of oceanography • Research techniques • Geology of the ocean • Properties of the ocean
LIFEPAC 9	**HUMAN ANATOMY II** • Respiratory system • Circulatory system • Digestive system • Endocrine system	**BALANCE IN NATURE** • Photosynthesis • Food • Natural cycles • Balance in nature	**SCIENCE AND TOMORROW** • The land • Waste and ecology • Industry and energy • New frontiers
LIFEPAC 10	**CAREERS IN SCIENCE** • Scientists at work • Astronomy • Meteorology • Medicine	**SCIENCE AND TECHNOLOGY** • Basic science • Physical science • Life science • Vocations in science	**SCIENTIFIC APPLICATIONS** • Measurement • Practical health • Geology and astronomy • Solving problems

Grade 10	Grade 11	Grade 12	
TAXONOMY • History of taxonomy • Binomial nomenclature • Classification • Taxonomy	**INTRODUCTION TO CHEMISTRY** • Metric units and instrumentation • Observation and hypothesizing • Scientific notation • Careers in chemistry	**KINEMATICS** • Scalars and vectors • Length measurement • Acceleration • Fields and models	LIFEPAC 1
BASIS OF LIFE • Elements and molecules • Properties of compounds • Chemical reactions • Organic compounds	**BASIC CHEMICAL UNITS** • Alchemy • Elements • Compounds • Mixtures	**DYNAMICS** • Newton's Laws of Motion • Gravity • Circular motion • Kepler's Laws of Motion	LIFEPAC 2
MICROBIOLOGY • The microscope • Protozoan • Algae • Microorganisms	**GASES AND MOLES** • Kinetic theory • Gas laws • Combined gas law • Moles	**WORK AND ENERGY** • Mechanical energy • Conservation of energy • Power and efficiency • Heat energy	LIFEPAC 3
CELLS • Cell theories • Examination of the cell • Cell design • Cells in organisms	**ATOMIC MODELS** • Historical models • Modern atomic structure • Periodic Law • Nuclear reactions	**WAVES** • Energy transfers • Reflection and refraction of waves • Diffraction and interference • Sound waves	LIFEPAC 4
PLANTS: GREEN FACTORIES • The plant cell • Anatomy of the plant • Growth and function of plants • Plants and people	**CHEMICAL FORMULAS** • Ionic charges • Electronegativity • Chemical bonds • Molecular shape	**LIGHT** • Speed of light • Mirrors • Lenses • Models of light	LIFEPAC 5
HUMAN ANATOMY AND PHYSIOLOGY • Digestive and excretory system • Respiratory and circulatory system • Skeletal and muscular system • Body control systems	**CHEMICAL REACTIONS** • Detecting reactions • Energy changes • Reaction rates • Equilibriums	**STATIC ELECTRICITY** • Nature of charges • Transfer of charges • Electric fields • Electric potential	LIFEPAC 6
INHERITANCE • Gregor Mendel's experiments • Chromosomes and heredity • Molecular genetics • Human genetics	**EQUILIBRIUM SYSTEMS** • Solutions • Solubility equilibriums • Acid-base equilibriums • Redox equilibriums	**CURRENT ELECTRICITY** • Electromotive force • Electron flow • Resistance • Circuits	LIFEPAC 7
CELL DIVISION & REPRODUCTION • Mitosis and meiosis • Asexual reproduction • Sexual reproduction • Plant reproduction	**HYDROCARBONS** • Organic compounds • Carbon atoms • Carbon bonds • Saturated and unsaturated	**MAGNETISM** • Fields • Forces • Electromagnetism • Electron beams	LIFEPAC 8
ECOLOGY & ENERGY • Ecosystems • Communities and habitats • Pollution • Energy	**CARBON CHEMISTRY** • Saturated and unsaturated • Reaction types • Oxygen groups • Nitrogen groups	**ATOMIC AND NUCLEAR PHYSICS** • Electromagnetic radiation • Quantum theory • Nuclear theory • Nuclear reaction	LIFEPAC 9
APPLICATIONS OF BIOLOGY • Principles of experimentation • Principles of reproduction • Principles of life • Principles of ecology	**ATOMS TO HYDROCARBONS** • Atoms and molecules • Chemical bonding • Chemical systems • Organic chemistry	**KINEMATICS TO NUCLEAR PHYSICS** • Mechanics • Wave motion • Electricity • Modern physics	LIFEPAC 10

_____

_____

_____

_____

_____

_____

_____

_____

_____

_____

_____

_____

_____

_____

_____

_____

_____

_____

_____

_____

_____

_____

_____

_____

_____

_____

_____

_____

_____

MANAGEMENT

STRUCTURE OF THE LIFEPAC CURRICULUM

The LIFEPAC curriculum is conveniently structured to provide one teacher handbook containing teacher support material with answer keys and ten student worktexts for each subject at grade levels two through twelve. The worktext format of the LIFEPACs allows the student to read the textual information and complete workbook activities all in the same booklet. The easy to follow LIFEPAC numbering system lists the grade as the first number(s) and the last two digits as the number of the series. For example, the Language Arts LIFEPAC at the 6th grade level, 5th book in the series would be LA 605.

Each LIFEPAC is divided into 3 to 5 sections and begins with an introduction or overview of the booklet as well as a series of specific learning objectives to give a purpose to the study of the LIFEPAC. The introduction and objectives are followed by a vocabulary section which may be found at the beginning of each section at the lower levels, at the beginning of the LIFEPAC in the middle grades, or in the glossary at the high school level. Vocabulary words are used to develop word recognition and should not be confused with the spelling words introduced later in the LIFEPAC. The student should learn all vocabulary words before working the LIFEPAC sections to improve comprehension, retention, and reading skills.

Each activity or written assignment has a number for easy identification, such as 1.1. The first number corresponds to the LIFEPAC section and the number to the right of the decimal is the number of the activity.

Teacher checkpoints, which are essential to maintain quality learning, are found at various locations throughout the LIFEPAC. The teacher should check 1) neatness of work and penmanship, 2) quality of understanding (tested with a short oral quiz), 3) thoroughness of answers (complete sentences and paragraphs, correct spelling, etc.), 4) completion of activities (no blank spaces), and 5) accuracy of answers as compared to the answer key (all answers correct).

The self test questions are also number coded for easy reference. For example, 2.015 means that this is the 15th question in the self test of Section II. The first number corresponds to the LIFEPAC section, the zero indicates that it is a self test question, and the number to the right of the zero the question number.

The LIFEPAC test is packaged at the centerfold of each LIFEPAC. It should be removed and put aside before giving the booklet to the student for study.

Answer and test keys have the same numbering system as the LIFEPACs and appear at the back of this handbook. The student may be given access to the answer keys (not the test keys) under teacher supervision so that he can score his own work.

A thorough study of the Curriculum Overview by the teacher before instruction begins is essential to the success of the student. The teacher should become familiar with expected skill mastery and understand how these grade level skills fit into the overall skill development of the curriculum. The teacher should also preview the objectives that appear at the beginning of each LIFEPAC for additional preparation and planning.

TEST SCORING and GRADING

Answer keys and test keys give examples of correct answers. They convey the idea, but the student may use many ways to express a correct answer. The teacher should check for the essence of the answer, not for the exact wording. Many questions are high level and require thinking and creativity on the part of the student. Each answer should be scored based on whether or not the main idea written by the student matches the model example. "Any Order" or "Either Order" in a key indicates that no particular order is necessary to be correct.

Most self tests and LIFEPAC tests at the lower elementary levels are scored at 1 point per answer; however, the upper levels may have a point system awarding 2 to 5 points for various answers or questions. Further, the total test points will vary; they may not always equal 100 points. They may be 78, 85, 100, 105, etc.

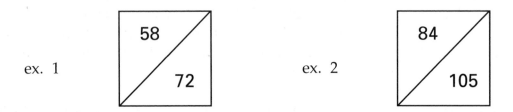

ex. 1   58 / 72   ex. 2   84 / 105

A score box similar to ex.1 above is located at the end of each self test and on the front of the LIFEPAC test. The bottom score, 72, represents the total number of points possible on the test. The upper score, 58, represents the number of points your student will need to receive an 80% or passing grade. If you wish to establish the exact percentage that your student has achieved, find the total points of his correct answers and divide it by the bottom number (in this case 72). For example, if your student has a point total of 65, divide 65 by 72 for a grade of 90%. Referring to ex. 2, on a test with a total of 105 possible points, the student would have to receive a minimum of 84 correct points for an 80% or passing grade. If your student has received 93 points, simply divide the 93 by 105 for a percentage grade of 89%. Students who receive a score below 80% should review the LIFEPAC and retest using the appropriate Alternate Test found in the Teacher's Guide.

The following is a guideline to assign letter grades for completed LIFEPACs based on a maximum total score of 100 points.

LIFEPAC Test   =   60% of the Total Score (or percent grade)
Self Test   =   25% of the Total Score (average percent of self tests)
Reports   =   10% or 10* points per LIFEPAC
Oral Work   =   5% or 5* points per LIFEPAC
*Determined by the teacher's subjective evaluation of the student's daily work.

Example:

LIFEPAC Test Score	=	92%	92 x .60	=	55 points
Self Test Average	=	90%	90 x .25	=	23 points
Reports				=	8 points
Oral Work				=	4 points

TOTAL POINTS   =   90 points

Grade Scale based on point system:

100	–	94	=	A
93	–	86	=	B
85	–	77	=	C
76	–	70	=	D
Below		70	=	F

TEACHER HINTS and STUDYING TECHNIQUES

LIFEPAC Activities are written to check the level of understanding of the preceding text. The student may look back to the text as necessary to complete these activities; however, a student should never attempt to do the activities without reading (studying) the text first. Self tests and LIFEPAC tests are never open book tests.

Language arts activities (skill integration) often appear within other subject curriculum. The purpose is to give the student an opportunity to test his skill mastery outside of the context in which it was presented.

Writing complete answers (paragraphs) to some questions is an integral part of the LIFEPAC Curriculum in all subjects. This builds communication and organization skills, increases understanding and retention of ideas, and helps enforce good penmanship. Complete sentences should be encouraged for this type of activity. Obviously, single words or phrases do not meet the intent of the activity, since multiple lines are given for the response.

Review is essential to student success. Time invested in review where review is suggested will be time saved in correcting errors later. Self tests, unlike the section activities, are closed book. This procedure helps to identify weaknesses before they become too great to overcome. Certain objectives from self tests are cumulative and test previous sections; therefore, good preparation for a self test must include all material studied up to that testing point.

The following procedure checklist has been found to be successful in developing good study habits in the LIFEPAC curriculum.

1. Read the introduction and Table of Contents.
2. Read the objectives.
3. Recite and study the entire vocabulary (glossary) list.
4. Study each section as follows:
    a. Read the introduction and study the section objectives.
    b. Read all the text for the entire section, but answer none of the activities.
    c. Return to the beginning of the section and memorize each vocabulary word and definition.
    d. Reread the section, complete the activities, check the answers with the answer key, correct all errors, and have the teacher check.
    e. Read the self test but do not answer the questions.
    f. Go to the beginning of the first section and reread the text and answers to the activities up to the self test you have not yet done.
    g. Answer the questions to the self test without looking back.
    h. Have the self test checked by the teacher.
    i. Correct the self test and have the teacher check the corrections.
    j. Repeat steps a–i for each section.

5. Use the SQ3R* method to prepare for the LIFEPAC test.
6. Take the LIFEPAC test as a closed book test.
7. LIFEPAC tests are administered and scored under direct teacher supervision. Students who receive scores below 80% should review the LIFEPAC using the SQ3R* study method and take the Alternate Test located in the Teacher Handbook. The final test grade may be the grade on the Alternate Test or an average of the grades from the original LIFEPAC test and the Alternate Test.

     *SQ3R: **S**can the whole LIFEPAC.

           Question yourself on the objectives.

           Read the whole LIFEPAC again.

           Recite through an oral examination.

           Review weak areas.

GOAL SETTING and SCHEDULES

Each school must develop its own schedule, because no single set of procedures will fit every situation. The following is an example of a daily schedule that includes the five LIFEPAC subjects as well as time slotted for special activities.

Possible Daily Schedule

8:15	–	8:25	Pledges, prayer, songs, devotions, etc.
8:25	–	9:10	Bible
9:10	–	9:55	Language Arts
9:55	–	10:15	Recess (juice break)
10:15	–	11:00	Mathematics
11:00	–	11:45	Social Studies
11:45	–	12:30	Lunch, recess, quiet time
12:30	–	1:15	Science
1:15	–		Drill, remedial work, enrichment*

*Enrichment: Computer time, physical education, field trips, fun reading, games and puzzles, family business, hobbies, resource persons, guests, crafts, creative work, electives, music appreciation, projects.

Basically, two factors need to be considered when assigning work to a student in the LIFEPAC curriculum.

The first is time. An average of 45 minutes should be devoted to each subject, each day. Remember, this is only an average. Because of extenuating circumstances a student may spend only 15 minutes on a subject one day and the next day spend 90 minutes on the same subject.

The second factor is the number of pages to be worked in each subject. A single LIFEPAC is designed to take 3 to 4 weeks to complete. Allowing about 3-4 days for LIFEPAC introduction, review, and tests, the student has approximately 15 days to complete the LIFEPAC pages. Simply take the number of pages in the LIFEPAC, divide it by 15 and you will have the number of pages that must be completed on a daily basis to keep the student on schedule. For example, a LIFEPAC containing 45 pages will require 3 completed pages per day. Again, this is only an average. While working a 45 page LIFEPAC, the student may complete only 1 page the first day if the text has a lot of activities or reports, but go on to complete 5 pages the next day.

Long range planning requires some organization. Because the traditional school year originates in the early fall of one year and continues to late spring of the following year, a calendar should be devised that covers this period of time. Approximate beginning and completion dates can be noted on the calendar as well as special occasions such as holidays, vacations, and birthdays. Since each LIFEPAC takes 3-4 weeks or eighteen days to complete, it should take about 180 school days to finish a set of ten LIFEPACs. Starting at the beginning school date, mark off eighteen school days on the calendar and that will become the targeted completion date for the first LIFEPAC. Continue marking the calendar until you have established dates for the remaining nine LIFEPACs making adjustments for previously noted holidays and vacations. If all five subjects are being used, the ten established target dates should be the same for the LIFEPACs in each subject.

FORMS

The sample weekly lesson plan and student grading sheet forms are included in this section as teacher support materials and may be duplicated at the convenience of the teacher.

The student grading sheet is provided for those who desire to follow the suggested guidelines for assignment of letter grades found on page 15. The student's self test scores should be posted as percentage grades. When the LIFEPAC is completed the teacher should average the self test grades, multiply the average by .25 and post the points in the box marked self test points. The LIFEPAC percentage grade should be multiplied by .60 and posted. Next, the teacher should award and post points for written reports and oral work. A report may be any type of written work assigned to the student whether it is a LIFEPAC or additional learning activity. Oral work includes the student's ability to respond orally to questions which may or may not be related to LIFEPAC activities or any type of oral report assigned by the teacher. The points may then be totaled and a final grade entered along with the date that the LIFEPAC was completed.

The Student Record Book which was specifically designed for use with the Alpha Omega curriculum provides space to record weekly progress for one student over a nine week period as well as a place to post self test and LIFEPAC scores. The Student Record Books are available through the current Alpha Omega catalog; however, unlike the enclosed forms these books are not for duplication and should be purchased in sets of four to cover a full academic year.

WEEKLY LESSON PLANNER

Week of:

Subject	Subject	Subject	Subject
Monday			

Subject	Subject	Subject	Subject
Tuesday			

Subject	Subject	Subject	Subject
Wednesday			

Subject	Subject	Subject	Subject
Thursday			

Subject	Subject	Subject	Subject
Friday			

WEEKLY LESSON PLANNER

Week of:

	Subject	Subject	Subject	Subject
Monday				
Tuesday				
Wednesday				
Thursday				
Friday				

Student Name _____   Year _____

Bible

LP #	Self Test Scores by Sections 1	2	3	4	5	Self Test Points	LIFEPAC Test	Oral Points	Report Points	Final Grade	Date
01											
02											
03											
04											
05											
06											
07											
08											
09											
10											

History & Geography

LP #	Self Test Scores by Sections 1	2	3	4	5	Self Test Points	LIFEPAC Test	Oral Points	Report Points	Final Grade	Date
01											
02											
03											
04											
05											
06											
07											
08											
09											
10											

Language Arts

LP #	Self Test Scores by Sections 1	2	3	4	5	Self Test Points	LIFEPAC Test	Oral Points	Report Points	Final Grade	Date
01											
02											
03											
04											
05											
06											
07											
08											
09											
10											

Student Name _____   Year _____

Mathematics

LP #	Self Test Scores by Sections 1	2	3	4	5	Self Test Points	LIFEPAC Test	Oral Points	Report Points	Final Grade	Date
01											
02											
03											
04											
05											
06											
07											
08											
09											
10											

Science

LP #	Self Test Scores by Sections 1	2	3	4	5	Self Test Points	LIFEPAC Test	Oral Points	Report Points	Final Grade	Date
01											
02											
03											
04											
05											
06											
07											
08											
09											
10											

Spelling/Electives

LP #	Self Test Scores by Sections 1	2	3	4	5	Self Test Points	LIFEPAC Test	Oral Points	Report Points	Final Grade	Date
01											
02											
03											
04											
05											
06											
07											
08											
09											
10											

**N
O
T
E
S**

INSTRUCTIONS FOR FIRST GRADE SCIENCE

The first grade handbooks of the LIFEPAC curriculum are designed to provide a step-by step procedure that will help the teacher prepare for and present each lesson effectively. In the early LIFEPACs the teacher should read the directions and any other sentences to the children. However, as the school year progresses, the student should be encouraged to begin reading and following his own instructional material in preparation for the independent study approach that begins at the second grade level.

This section of the *Teacher's Guide* includes the following teacher aids: 1) Cumulative Word List 2) Teacher Instruction Pages.

The Cumulative Word List is made up of words introduced at least once in one of the ten subject LIFEPACs. An asterisk (*) following a word indicates a direction-word that the children will need to know by sight to complete the work independently. Sight words are words that either are needed before their phonetic presentation or do not follow the standard phonetic rules. These words need to be learned through memorization and children should be drilled on them frequently. The drill may be done by use of a chart posted in a prominent place, by word card drills, word recognition or meaning games. Some words on the Cumulative Word List are not expected to be part of the student's reading vocabulary but part of his speaking vocabulary for better understanding of subject content.

The Teacher Instruction Pages list the Concept to be taught as well as Student Objectives and Goals for the Teacher. The Teaching Page contains directions for teaching that page. Worksheet pages used in some lessons follow this section and may be duplicated for individual student use. The Activities section at the end of each lesson is optional and may be used to reinforce or expand the concepts taught.

Materials needed are usually items such as pencils and crayons which are readily available. Additional items that may be required are LIFEPAC tablets (purchased through the catalog or may be any lined paper), alphabet cards, color and number charts, and flash cards for vocabulary words.

Page 1: Growing Up Healthy

CONCEPT: growing up healthy

OBJECTIVE: To introduce all the objectives.

PROCESSES: observing, predicting

READING INTEGRATION: main idea

VOCABULARY: healthy, sleep, exercise

MATERIALS NEEDED: books on health

TEACHING PAGE 1:

Distribute the LIFEPACs and give the children a little time to look through them.

Ask the children to volunteer their ideas of what they will learn in this LIFEPAC.

Present the vocabulary words.

Have the children follow along as you read the introduction and the objectives. If you wish have them read by the children. Stress that the objectives list things they will be able to do when LIFEPAC 106 is complete.

ACTIVITY:

Prepare a reading table. Find books about good health. Include foods, sleep, and exercise. These books may be used as read-aloud and free time reading. Those children who are able may use them as reference for report writing and for other independent projects.

GROWING UP HEALTHY

Meet Dan.
Dan will go with you through this LIFEPAC.
Dan will help you see how things grow.
Dan will help you learn how to grow up healthy.

 Objectives

1. I can name three things that grow.
2. I can tell two ways that I am growing.
3. I can name five foods that are good for me.
4. I can show two exercises that are good for me.
5. I can tell how much sleep I need.

page 1 (one)

I. PART ONE
Pages 2 and 3: Growing

CONCEPT: plants, animals, and people grow

OBJECTIVE: I can name three things that grow.

PROCESS: observing

READING INTEGRATION: recalling details, irregular verbs (grow/grew)

VOCABULARY: kitten, deer, cub, grew, living, (plants, animals, people, garden, bear)

MATERIALS NEEDED: pencils, LIFEPAC Tablet, Worksheet 1, scissors, glue

TEACHING PAGES 2 and 3:
Remind the children that the last two LIFEPACs were about things that grow.
Ask: "Can you name some things that grow that you learned about in LIFEPACs 104 and 105?" (plants, animals)
Tell the children that the first section of the LIFEPAC will review a few of the things they learned in Science 104 and 105 and then help them learn some ways people grow.
Present the vocabulary. Stress the irregular past tense of grow (grew).
Read the introductory sentences to the class or have them read by a volunteer.
Ask the class to identify the vocabulary words.
Continue to read through the page. Have the children recall and discuss the growing seed. They may have grown a plant in LIFEPAC 105, so will be able to talk about how it grew.
Read the sentences on page 3 to the class or have them read by students.
Continue discussion of how animals grow. Review names of baby animals with the names of their grown-up versions.

I. GROWING

All living things grow.
Plants grow.
Animals grow.
People grow.

PLANTS AND ANIMALS GROW

Look at the seed.
Dan put the seed in the garden.

Dan watered the seed.
The seed grew.
The seed grew into a plant.

page 2 (two)

Look at Tat.
Tat is Dan's kitten.
Tat is growing.
As Tat grows, she gets bigger.
Soon Tat will be a cat.

Match the small plant or animal to what it will be when it grows bigger.

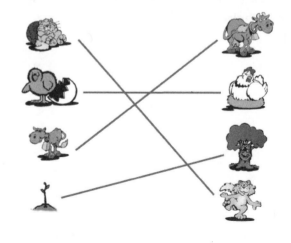

page 3 (three)

Examples: puppy/dog
   calf/cow
   fawn/deer
   chick/ hen, rooster, chicken
   cub/ bear
   colt/ horse

Go over the directions for the exercise. Put an example on the board. Use a puppy and dog, pictures or words. Draw a line to match.

Have the children complete the exercise independently. Check it together.

ACTIVITIES:

1.   Do Worksheet 1.

Read the sentences with the children.

Instruct the children to find the words that finish the sentence, to cut these words out, and to paste them in the right place.

Have the children read the sentences and talk about the animals.

2.   In the Tablet, have the children write these sentences.

"That will grow to be a cat."

"A seed will grow to be a plant."

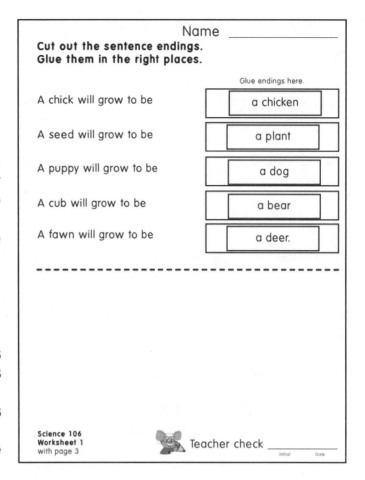

Name _____

Cut out the sentence endings.
Glue them in the right places.

Glue endings here.

A chick will grow to be	a chicken
A seed will grow to be	a plant
A puppy will grow to be	a dog
A cub will grow to be	a bear
A fawn will grow to be	a deer.

Science 106
Worksheet 1
with page 3

Teacher check _____
Initial   Date

31

Pages 4 and 5: Food to Grow

CONCEPTS: Review what plants and animals need to grow. Plants need water, sunlight, and good fertile soil (dirt). Animals must have food.

OBJECTIVE: I can name three things that grow.

PROCESS: observing

READING INTEGRATION: listening, rhyming, recalling details

VOCABULARY: sunshine, picnic, treat, lunch, munch (rain)

MATERIALS NEEDED: LIFEPAC Tablet, pencils

TEACHING PAGES 4 and 5:
　　Present the vocabulary words.
　　Prepare the children for listening.
　　Have them listen for the rhyming words and the vocabulary words.
　　Have them think as they listen about what living things need in order to grow.
　　Read the poem aloud.
　　Read it again as the children follow along.
　　Discussion questions:
　　"What else do plants need to grow besides rain and sunshine?" (good fertile dirt)
　　"What do cows and horses eat?" (from Science 104-hay, grass, and so on)
　　"What do pigs eat?" (from Science 104-corn)
　　"What do ants eat when there is no picnic?"
　　"What do you eat?"
　　Before page 5, reread the poem from page 4 to help the children remember it. Have the children follow along.
　　Have a child read the directions. If necessary, have each sentence read, too.
　　Have the children complete the page.

What's for Lunch?

Sunshine and rain
Will help grow a plant.
But the rain and the sun
Cannot grow an ant.

Like all other animals
Ants need to eat.
For children and ants
A picnic's a treat.

Sometimes I wonder
Just what the ants munch
On all of the days
That I stay home for lunch.

page 4 (four)

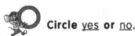 **Circle** <u>yes</u> **or** <u>no</u>.

An ant is a plant.	yes /	(no)
Plants like picnics.	yes /	(no)
Rain helps plants grow.	(yes) /	no
Children need to eat.	(yes) /	no

page 5 (five)

ACTIVITY:
Have the children choose an animal and find out what it eats. They should write a sentence or a short paragraph about it in their Tablets.

Pages 6 and 7: Growing

CONCEPT: a child grows bigger

OBJECTIVE: I can tell two ways that I am growing.

PROCESSES: observing, predicting

READING INTEGRATION: main idea, recalling details, following directions

VOCABULARY: body, taller, bigger

MATERIALS NEEDED: yard or meter stick, pictures of baby and grown animals, crayons, LIFEPAC tablet, pencil

TEACHING PAGES 6 and 7:

Show the class the picture of the young and grown animals. Ask the children to tell ways the animals grow. (bigger, stronger).

Present the vocabulary.

Read the title and introduction to the class or have the children read it aloud.

Ask: "How can you tell that you are getting bigger and taller?" Have the children volunteer ideas.

Remind the children of how they have already grown, and how they will grow much more.

Read the direction on page 7.

Have the children draw themselves as they were (baby), as they are now, and as they think they will be when they grow up.

ACTIVITIES:

1. Using inches or centimeters, measure each child in the class. Make a chart or graph showing the height of each child. Measure again later in the school year to demonstrate growth.

2. Make a bulletin board with baby pictures of all the children in the class, if they are available. Number the pictures. Ask the children to try to name each child. Post a class list to help with the spelling. Provide paper for the guessing game.

YOUR BODY GROWS

You are growing.
You are taller now
than you were
four years ago.

Dan is growing.
Dan will grow
to be a man.
As Dan grows,
he gets bigger.
As you grow,
you get bigger.

page 6 (six)

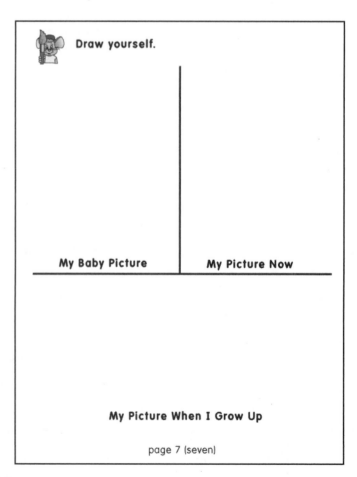

Draw yourself.

My Baby Picture | My Picture Now

My Picture When I Grow Up

page 7 (seven)

3. Have the children write and complete this sentence in their Tablets:

When I grow up I will be _____. Put the sentence on the board. Help with the spelling of words needed to complete the sentence.

Page 8: You Grow

CONCEPT: Children grow in the ways they behave.

OBJECTIVE: I can tell two ways that I am growing.

PROCESSES: observing, comparing

READING INTEGRATION: main idea

VOCABULARY: act, share, (learn, change)

MATERIALS NEEDED: Worksheet 2, crayons

TEACHING PAGE 8:

Tell the children that they can grow in many ways. Their bodies grow. Their minds grow by learning many new things. They can learn to act in ways that make others happy.

Read the sentences with the children. Ask if they can remember how they used to act when they were very little.

Allow discussion time to compare ways they used to behave with the way they behave now. Ask them how they have changed the way they act.

ACTIVITY:

Do Worksheet 2.

Read the direction. Talk about how the baby should grow up.

Have the children trace the maze with their fingers before they trace it with the crayon.

YOU GROW

As you grow up,
your body grows taller.
You grow up in other ways, too.
You learn to share.
You learn to help others.
You change the way you act.

page 8 (eight)

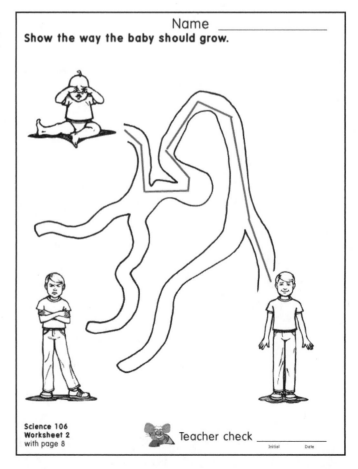

Name _____

Show the way the baby should grow.

Science 106
Worksheet 2
with page 8

Teacher check _____
Initial   Date

Pages 9 and 10: Activity Pages

VOCABULARY: sad, happy

MATERIALS NEEDED: pencils, Worksheet 3, crayons, LIFEPAC Tablet

TEACHING PAGES 9 and 10:

Put a happy face and a sad face on the board.

Present the vocabulary using the word cards.

Ask the children to tell which word goes with each face.

Fasten *happy* under the smiling face.

Fasten *sad* under the frowning face.

Have the children tell some things they do that make other people happy or sad.

Page 9: Read the direction and the sentences with the children. Have them complete each face. Discuss why they completed the faces as they did.

Reinforce the idea that the child's behavior can grow as well as his size.

Page 10: Have the directions read by a volunteer.

Have the children complete the page.

ACTIVITIES:

1.   Do Worksheet 3.

Read the direction to the children.

Make sure they know what to do.

When they have finished, have each child talk about his pictures and explain what happy thing he will do for someone else.

Have each child write a few paragraphs about his picture in his Tablet. Help with spelling.

2.   Write these sentences on the board.

I can make someone happy.

I can make someone sad.

Have the children write them in their Tablets.

page 9 (nine)

page 10 (ten)

Name _____

Draw a 😊 **thing you can do.**

Science 106
Worksheet 3
with page 10

Teacher check _____
Initial   Date

Page 11: Activity Page

MATERIALS NEEDED: pencils, LIFEPAC Tablet

TEACHING PAGE 11:

Review the words from Section 1. Review the baby and grown-up animals, plants, and people.

Read or have volunteers read the directions.

Let the children complete the page independently. Check it together. Use the time to discuss concepts taught in the LIFEPAC.

Be sure that the children write the sentence in their Tablets.

At this point the children should look back through their LIFEPACs to prepare for the self test.

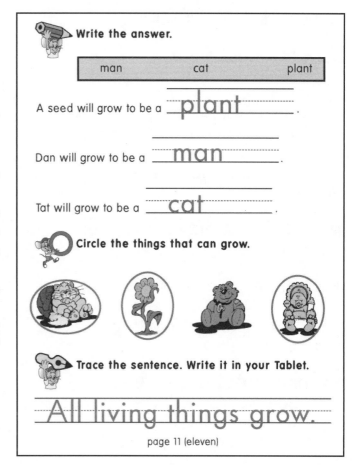

39

Pages 12 and 13: Self Test 1

CONCEPT: evaluation

OBJECTIVES:
I can name three things that grow.
I can tell two ways that I am growing.

TEACHER GOAL: To check each child's progress.

READING INTEGRATION: following directions, recalling details

VOCABULARY: Review all vocabulary.

MATERIALS NEEDED: pencils, Worksheets 4 and 5

TEACHING PAGES 12 and 13:
Provide additional review of vocabulary words and concepts.

Practice matching vocabulary to pictures.

Read all directions with the children. Be sure that they are understood.

The general proficiency of your group should dictate whether you choose to direct the self test or allow the children to proceed independently, once directions are given.

In either case you should be available to answer questions and to help with the vocabulary as needed.

Check immediately. Review any concepts that were missed.

ACTIVITIES:
1.   Do Worksheet 4.
Read the first two sentences or have a child read them.

Tell them to follow the dots from number to number to see what the tadpole will become.

2.   Do Worksheet 5.
Read the two sentences. Talk about caterpillars. Ask how many have seen a caterpillar. Ask if any of the children have

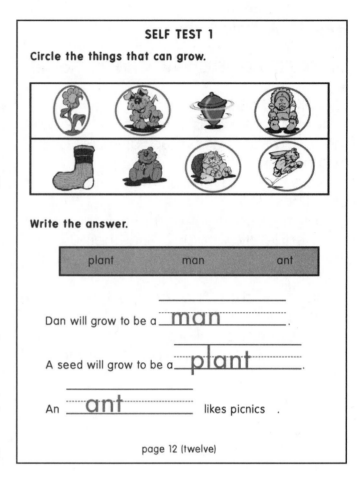

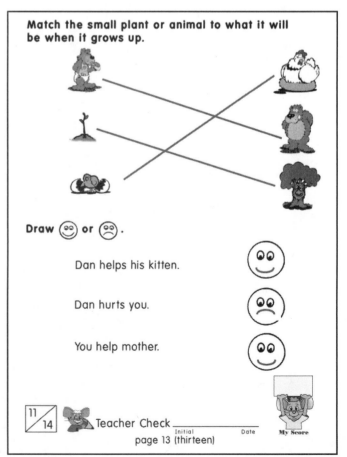

ever watched a caterpillar spin a cocoon and turn into a new thing.

Tell them to follow the dots to find what the caterpillar becomes.

Talk about butterflies and moths.

Name _____

Here is a baby animal.
See what it will grow up to be.

tadpole

Follow the dots.
Color the pictures.

Science 106
Worksheet 4
with page 13

Teacher check _____
Initial   Date

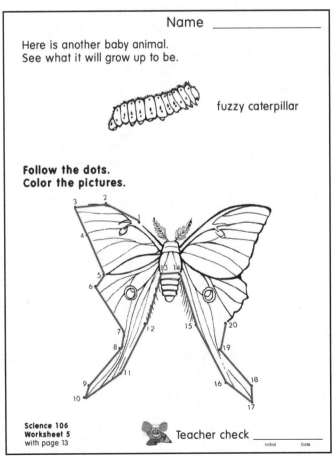

Name _____

Here is another baby animal.
See what it will grow up to be.

fuzzy caterpillar

Follow the dots.
Color the pictures.

Science 106
Worksheet 5
with page 13

Teacher check _____
Initial   Date

II. PART TWO
Page 14: Eating and Sleeping

CONCEPT: Good food and sleep help you grow up to be healthy.

OBJECTIVE: I can name five foods that are good for me.

PROCESS: observing

BIBLE REFERENCE: 1 Corinthians 3:16 and 17; 6:19

READING INTEGRATION: main idea, recalling details

VOCABULARY: strong, stronger, good, better, snack

MATERIALS NEEDED: Worksheet 6, pencils, crayons

TEACHING PAGE 14:

Section Two of LIFEPAC 106 will help the children understand the importance of good nutrition and proper rest. The section will include some in-class food projects as part of the activities. You may wish to add others of your own.

Prepare the children for the section by telling them that the next section will help them to understand how important it is to eat well and get enough sleep. Discuss Bible references like I Corinthians 3:16 and 17 and 1 Corinthians 6: 19.

Ask: "How well can you do in school if you stay up too late?" "How do you feel at school if you go without breakfast?"

"What do you think you would be like if you never had enough to eat or enough sleep?"

Read through the sentences with the children. You may want to have the children read the sentences aloud. Allow discussion time.

II. EATING AND SLEEPING

To grow up healthy,
you need to eat the right food.
You need to get enough
sleep, too.

Dan will help you
to know what to eat.
He will help you
to know how much sleep
you need.

HEALTHY FOOD

To grow bigger
and stronger,
you must eat healthy food.
Some foods
help you grow
better than other foods.

page 14 (fourteen)

ACTIVITY:

Do Worksheet 6.

Children are to take these home and keep a record of food they eat for one week. The parents should help keep this record.

Name _____
Foods I Eat

	Breakfast	Lunch	Dinner	Snacks
Day 1				
Day 2				
Day 3				
Day 4				
Day 5				

Science 106
Worksheet 6
with page 14

Teacher check _____
Initial   Date

Pages 15 and 16: Balanced Meals

CONCEPTS: breakfast, lunch, and dinner; balanced meals

OBJECTIVE: I can name five foods that are good for me.

PROCESS: observing

READING INTEGRATION: picture interpretation, following directions, recalling details

VOCABULARY: breakfast, lunch, dinner

MATERIALS NEEDED: Worksheets 7 and 8; crayons; pictures of foods for breakfast, lunch, and dinner

TEACHING PAGES 15 and 16:
Read the sentence at the top.
Discuss each picture and point out what makes up a well balanced meal.
Present the vocabulary. Use the word cards to match with the pictures of the foods associated with each meal.
Have volunteers tell what they ate for breakfast, lunch, and dinner yesterday.
Read the direction on page 16 and have the children complete the page independently.
Discuss the pictures the children have drawn and the foods they eat.

ACTIVITIES:

1.   Make a list of nutritious foods for each meal of the day. Include snack foods, too. Use chart paper. Be sure the lists include foods from the main food groups: dairy (milk and milk products), meat (also fish and fowl, cheese, eggs), grains (breads and cereals), vegetables, and fruits.
2.   Do Worksheet 7.
Prepare *"Super Peanut Butter"* in class. Serve on celery sticks. This makes an excellent after school snack.

You need three good meals each day.

breakfast

lunch

dinner

page 15 (fifteen)

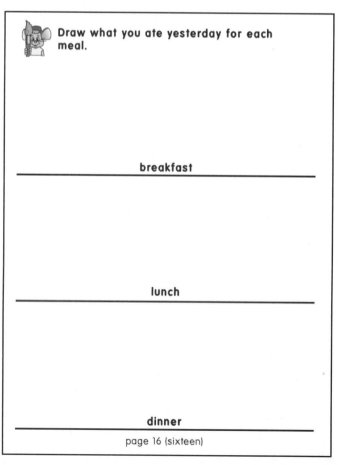

Draw what you ate yesterday for each meal.

breakfast

lunch

dinner

page 16 (sixteen)

Memory verse for the children to learn and recite. Put the verse on the board for the children to copy. Have them cut the memory verse off the Worksheet and take it home.

3. Do Worksheet 8.

Before the children color the picture, talk about why the boy looks as he does. The illustration is a demonstration that everything the children eat turns into part of them. Emphasize the importance of eating a proper diet.

Have the children color the picture.

4. Discuss snack foods. Have the children contribute ideas of what snacks would be good for them.

Name _____

Super Peanut Butter

1 pound salt peanuts without shells
1/4 cup wheat germ
1/4 cup honey

Grind the peanuts.
Add the wheat germ and honey.
Stir until smooth.
Serve on celery sticks.

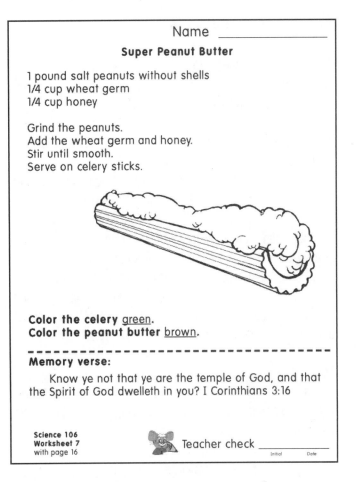

Color the celery green.
Color the peanut butter brown.

- -
Memory verse:

Know ye not that ye are the temple of God, and that the Spirit of God dwelleth in you? I Corinthians 3:16

Science 106
Worksheet 7
with page 16

Teacher check _____
Initial   Date

Color the picture.

Name _____

Science 106
Worksheet 8
with page 16

Teacher check _____
Initial   Date

Page 17: Activity Page

MATERIALS NEEDED: pencils, crayons, food pictures, chart paper, lists from page 16 (Activity 1), LIFEPAC Tablet

TEACHING PAGE 17:

Review the lists from page 16.

Make a new chart of foods children like that are not really good for them.

Title the chart: NOT SO GOOD FOODS

Explain that this page has pictures of good and "not so good" foods.

Have a volunteer read the directions.

Let the children complete the page independently. Check it together and discuss the question at the bottom.

ACTIVITY:

Put these sentences on the board. Have the children write and complete them in their Tablets. Help with spelling.

Good food helps me_____

My favorite breakfast food is_____

For lunch I like_____

Circle the food that is good for you.

Circle <u>yes</u> **or** <u>no</u>.

Did you choose healthy foods?   yes   no

page 17 (seventeen)

Page 18: Healthy Foods

CONCEPT: A meal should include good healthy food.

OBJECTIVE: I can name five foods that are good for me.

PROCESS: comparing

READING INTEGRATION: listening, rhyming, main idea

VOCABULARY: meat, milk, supper, (bread, fruit, vegetables, dinner)

MATERIALS NEEDED: Worksheet 9, food for stew

TEACHING PAGE 18:

Discuss the fact that people living in different kinds of communities call their meals by different names. Many farm families have their main meal at noon and call it dinner. The later meal is called supper. They do this because the whole family eats together at noon. Many families have their big Sunday dinner at noon, no matter where they live. In cities and other places where the whole family cannot eat together at noon, families have dinner in the early evening. These people have lunch at noon.

Prepare the children for listening. They should be able to tell the main idea of the poem.

Read the poem aloud.

Read it again.

Ask for a volunteer to tell the main idea of the poem.

ACTIVITIES:

1. Do Worksheet 9.

Draw the hands on the clock to show the time you eat dinner.

If your group has had no experience with telling time, draw clock faces on the

---

Meal-Time Mix-Up

Some folks have their dinner
At noon when the sun is high.
Some others have their dinner
When night is almost nigh.

If you have your supper
When it's almost time for bed,
You probably have your dinner
When I have lunch instead.

Whatever you call your meal,
Or whenever you might eat,
You should have some vegetables,
Bread, milk, fruit, and meat.

page 18 (eighteen)

---

board to show the times most children have dinner.

Children may use the clocks they made in Social Studies 106 for further practice.

2.   Plan a snack-size class dinner. You make a soup or stew. Parents would probably be willing to provide the ingredients.

To provide a *1/4 - 1/2 cup size serving per child* for 30 children you will need:

1 1/2 pounds inexpensive stew beef, dredged in seasoned flour, diced and browned ahead of time
    6 potatoes, peeled and diced
    3 -6 carrots, cleaned and diced
    6 - 10 tomatoes, cut in small pieces
    1 - 2 onions, diced
The ingredients below are optional:
    1 small turnip, diced
    2 parsnips, diced
    peas - fresh, frozen, or canned
    corn - fresh, frozen, or canned

Add to all the above ingredients 3 cups of water (add more if needed).

Gather the class around early in the morning to watch and help prepare the vegetables. Sharp knives should be avoided but children can handle most peelers.

Place the pre-browned meat into a large roaster, stew pot, or crock pot. (You may need two).

Add the cleaned, diced vegetables and the water.

Salt lightly as needed. Add a bay leaf for extra flavor.

Let the stew simmer slowly until 30 minutes before time to go home.

Serve in small unwaxed paper cups. Give each child a plastic spoon or fork and a napkin.

You may want to include soda crackers as part of the "dinner".

As you prepare and serve the stew, discuss the nutritional value of such a meal. It includes both meat and vegetables. The crackers are made from grain. With a glass of milk and fruit for desert the meal would include all of the food groups.

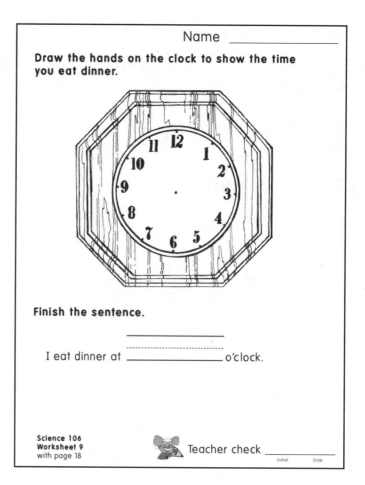

Name _____

Draw the hands on the clock to show the time you eat dinner.

Finish the sentence.

I eat dinner at _____ o'clock.

Science 106
Worksheet 9
with page 18

Teacher check _____
Initial   Date

48

Page 19: Breakfast

CONCEPT: You need a good breakfast for energy.

OBJECTIVE: I can name five foods that are good for me.

PROCESS: predicting, classifying

READING INTEGRATION: speaking in a group, following directions

VOCABULARY: energy

MATERIALS NEEDED: paper plates, breakfast foods, pencils

TEACHING PAGE 19:

Tell the children that no matter what the other meals are called the first meal of the day is probably called breakfast.

Present the vocabulary word. Have the children offer suggestions about what it might mean.

Have volunteers read the sentences. *Ask:* "If you have energy what can you do?" (run, play, work, think) "If you have no energy what can happen?" (you're tired, you can't learn as well, and so on)

"What can you do every morning to have enough energy?"

"How will this family feel after breakfast?" (have the children study the picture)

Have a child read the direction for the exercise. Let the children complete the page independently.

ACTIVITIES:

1. Give each child a white paper plate. Have the children choose a meal, breakfast, lunch, or dinner, and draw and color their favorite foods. Remind them to plan meals that are good for them.

2. You may wish to plan a class breakfast. Your menu could include pancakes with honey and a juice. If your budget allows, add sausage or bacon. You will need paper plates, cups, plastic tableware, and some volunteer cooks.

Breakfast is important, too.

Match the food with the meal.

breakfast

lunch

dinner

page 19 (nineteen)

Pages 20 and 21: Enough Sleep

CONCEPT: Everyone needs sleep to stay healthy.

OBJECTIVE: I can tell how much sleep I need.

PROCESS: observing, comparing

READING INTEGRATION: recalling details, main idea, listening, speaking in a group

VOCABULARY: rest, sleep, hours, grown

MATERIALS NEEDED: Worksheet 10, pencils. crayons, LIFEPAC Tablet

TEACHING PAGES 20 and 21:

Tell the children that good food alone will not keep your body healthy. A body needs sleep as well in order to recover from the hard work it must do each day.

Read through the entire page to the class, or have it read aloud by volunteers.

Provide discussion time. Use these questions:

"Why does your body need to rest and sleep?" (It works hard.)

"What does sleep do for you?" (It helps you stay healthy.)

"How much sleep do you need?" (ten hours)

"How much sleep do babies need?" (many hours)

"How much sleep do grown-ups need?" (eight hours)

"Where does Dan sleep?" (in his bed)

Have a child find and read the directions on page 21.

Read the words to be used and the sentences aloud if necessary. Have the children complete the page independently. Check it together. Discuss each item as a review for the self test.

ACTIVITIES:

1. Do Worksheet 10.

ENOUGH SLEEP

Your body works hard.
Your body needs rest.
You rest when you sleep.

You need sleep.
Sleep helps you
stay healthy.

Babies need to sleep
for many hours.
You need to have
ten hours of sleep
every day.

Grown-ups need
eight hours of sleep.

Dan sleeps in his bed.
Dan needs to rest.
Dan rests when he sleeps.

page 20 (twenty)

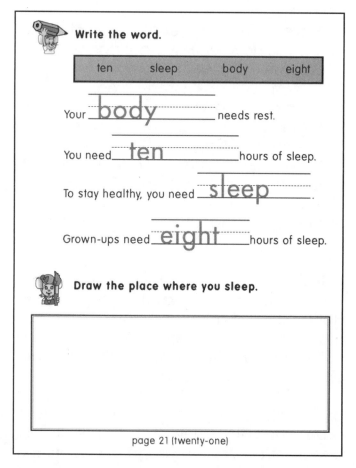

Write the word.

ten	sleep	body	eight

Your **body** needs rest.

You need **ten** hours of sleep.

To stay healthy, you need **sleep**

Grown-ups need **eight** hours of sleep.

Draw the place where you sleep.

page 21 (twenty-one)

Read the directions. Make sure the children understand the color key before they begin.

When they have finished, have them circle the answers to the question.

2.   Animals need sleep, too.

Have the children find books about an animal. Ask them to find out where and how long the animals sleep. They may write a sentence or paragraph about it in their Tablets.

Provide construction paper for the children to draw and color the animal sleeping.

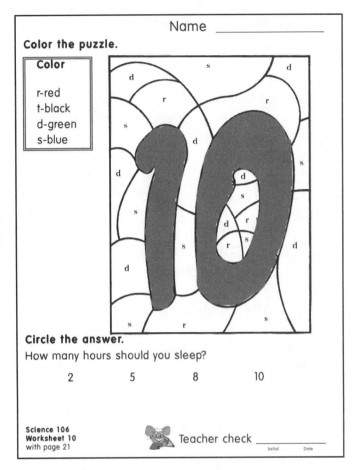

Name _____

Color the puzzle.

Color
r-red
t-black
d-green
s-blue

Circle the answer.

How many hours should you sleep?

2   5   8   10

Science 106
Worksheet 10
with page 21

Teacher check _____
Initial   Date

Pages 22 and 23: Self Test 2

OBJECTIVE:

I can name three things that grow.

I can tell two ways that I am growing.

I can name five foods that are good for me.

I can tell how much sleep I need.

TEACHER GOAL: To check each child's progress.

READING INTEGRATION: Following directions, recalling details

VOCABULARY: Review all vocabulary

TEACHING PAGES 22 AND 23

Review the vocabulary words and the concepts for sections one and two.

Ask these key questions:

"What will Dan grow up to be?"

(a man)

"What will his kitten grow up to be?"

(a cat)

"What else grows besides animals and people?"

(plants)

"How much sleep do you need?"

(ten hours)

"How much sleep do grown-ups need?"

(eight hours)

"How much sleep do babies need?"

(many hours)

"Name some foods that are good for you."

"In what ways can you grow?"

(size and behavior)

The general proficiency of your group will dictate whether you chose to direct the self test or allow the children to proceed independently, once the directions are given.

In either case you should be available to answer questions and to help with vocabulary, as needed.

Check together and review any concepts missed.

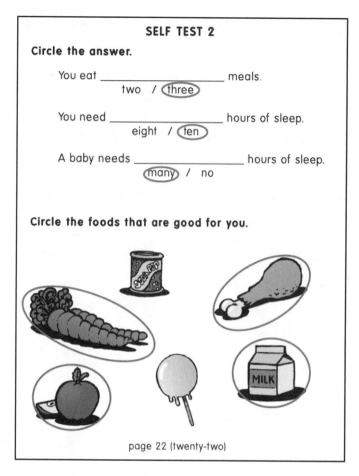

page 22 (twenty-two)

page 23 (twenty-three)

Have a parent or classroom helper go over the vocabulary and the concepts with those children who need extra help.

ACTIVITIES:

Do Worksheet 11.

Read the direction. Review the rebus pictures and any vocabulary the children do not know.

Let the children do the page independently.

Check together. Use as a review of the concepts.

Name _____

Circle the answer.

Plants, animals, and people can _____ .
grow / sleep

A grown-up needs _____ hours of sleep.
many / eight

Soda pop _____ good for you.
is / is not

Milk _____ good for you.
is / is not

A fawn will grow to be a _____ .
bear / deer

Science 106
Worksheet 11
with page 23

Teacher check _____
Initial   Date

III. PART THREE
Pages 24 and 25: Exercising

CONCEPT: Your body needs exercise.

OBJECTIVE: I can show two exercises that are good for me.

READING INTEGRATION: main idea, speaking in a group, following directions

VOCABULARY: exercise, playing

MATERIALS NEEDED: posters or pictures of ways people can get good exercise, banner paper, paint, brushes, water, Worksheet 12, LIFEPAC Tablet, pencils

TEACHING PAGES 24 and 25:
Tell the children that their bodies need even more than good food and enough sleep in order to grow strong and healthy.

Present the vocabulary words. Display the pictures. Have the children tell what the people are doing that provides exercise.

Read the page to the class, or have it read aloud by volunteers.

Ask these questions:

"Can you name three things your body needs to grow strong and healthy?" (food, sleep, exercise)

"Tell something you do that is good exercise." (give several children the chance to answer)

"If you ate good food, got plenty of sleep but always stayed in bed or in a chair, how would you feel?"

"Who might feel stronger, a man who works on a farm or a man who works in an office?"

"Why?"

"What could the person who works in the office do to feel strong?" (exercise)

Remind the children that many things they do provide them with the exercises they need to help them stay healthy.

III. EXERCISING

Your body needs
food and sleep.
Your body needs
exercise, too.

Dan will show you
exercises you do
each day.
He will show you
some special exercises
to build your body.

page 24 (twenty-four)

How Many Exercises?

Read the sentence with your teacher.

Playing is good exercise.

page 25 (twenty-five)

Have the children examine the pictures on page 25 and tell what the children are doing. (playing)

Ask: "Is anyone on the page not getting exercise?" (no)

Have the children count the exercises and write the number on the line. (6)

Ask a volunteer to read the directions. Read the sentence with the class.

Let the children complete the page independently.

ACTIVITIES:

1. Do Worksheet 12.

Read the directions.

Let the children complete the page independently.

Check together.

2. Begin a class mural or individual posters of children exercising. Provide banner paper, paint, brushes, and water. You might make this a "discovery center" activity. Give each child in the class a chance to participate in the project.

3. Have the children write the sentence in their Tablets.

Name _____

Write the words.

| exercise | healthy | playing |

playing _____ is good exercise.

exercise _____ helps you grow strong.

Food, sleep and exercise help you grow up

healthy _____ .

Color Dan playing.

Science 106
Worksheet 12
with page 25

Teacher check _____
Initial   Date

Pages 26 and 27: Exercise

CONCEPT: Ordinary activities are good exercises.

OBJECTIVE: I can show two exercises that are good for me.

PROCESSES: observing, comparing

READING INTEGRATION: recalling details, main idea

VOCABULARY: jump, run, skip, (walk)

MATERIALS NEEDED: pencils, Worksheet 13, crayons, LIFEPAC Tablet

TEACHING PAGES 26 and 27:

Tell the children that they have learned that playing is good exercise. As they go to school they probably walk, run, skip, or even jump over things as they go. All of these are good exercise, too. As you talk to the children, present the vocabulary words.

Read the page aloud or have it read by volunteers.

Have the children identify and demonstrate the vocabulary words. Have one child walk, another jump, one skip, and another run.

Ask these questions:

"Which activity might make you the most tired?"

"Which activity could you do the longest?"

"Which activity is the best exercise?" (all are good)

Have a child read the direction on page 27.

Have volunteers tell what Dan is doing in each picture.

Let the children complete the page independently. They may find the spelling of the words on page 26.

RUN, SKIP, JUMP, WALK

See Dan.
Dan can run,
skip, jump, and walk.
You can do that, too.
When you run, skip,
jump, or walk,
you are doing exercises.
Exercise is good for you.

page 26 (twenty-six)

Write the words for the picture.

Dan can jump .   Dan can run .

Dan can skip .   Dan can walk .

page 27 (twenty-seven)

ACTIVITIES:

1. Do Worksheet 13.
    Read the directions.
    Let the children do the page independently.
    Check together. Talk about proper shoes for running and playing.

2. Have the sentences on page 27 copied in the Tablets. Underline the vocabulary word in each sentence written.

3. Have a class field day. Plan relay races using skip, jump, run, and walk.

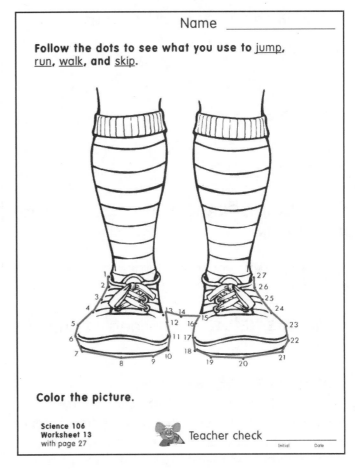

Name _____

Follow the dots to see what you use to <u>jump</u>, <u>run</u>, <u>walk</u>, **and** <u>skip</u>.

Color the picture.

Science 106
Worksheet 13
with page 27

Teacher check _____
Initial   Date

Pages 28 and 29: Special Exercises

CONCEPT: Special exercises help build strong bodies.

OBJECTIVE: I can name two exercises that are good for me.

PROCESS: observing

READING INTEGRATION: main idea, picture interpretation

VOCABULARY: muscles, jumping jack, toe-touch, sit- up, pushup

MATERIALS NEEDED: Worksheets 14 and 15, pencils, crayons

TEACHING PAGES 28 and 29:

Show the children that all the moving they do is done by muscles of the body. Muscles stretch and shorten to move the bones. Exercise helps to make the muscles strong and flexible.

The bicep muscle of the upper arm is a good one to use for demonstration. When the elbow is bent the bicep is short. As the elbow is straightened the muscle gets longer.

You may also use a rubber band to represent the lengthening and shortening of a muscle.

Page 28: Read the page to the class, or have it read by volunteers.

Present and display the vocabulary words as they appear in the text.

The next page will provide directions for doing the exercises.

Page 29: Have the children look at the pictures carefully. Have volunteers demonstrate each exercise. (Girls may do pushups leaving knees down if it is easier.)

Make room in the classroom or take the class out of doors or in a hallway for an exercise period.

Make an exercise period a regular part of the school day.

SPECIAL EXERCISES

Muscles move your body.
You need exercise
to keep your muscles healthy.
You need special exercises.
Dan will show you
four special exercises.
He will show you jumping jacks.
He will show you toe-touches.
He will show you sit-ups.
He will show you push ups.

page 28 (twenty-eight)

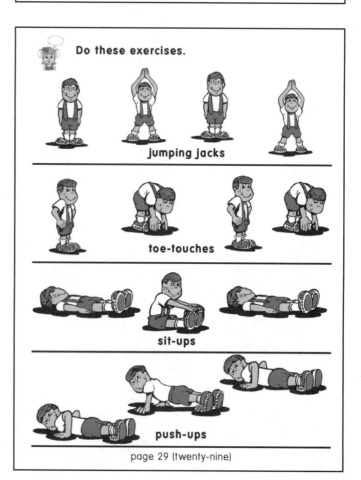

Do these exercises.

jumping jacks

toe-touches

sit-ups

push-ups

page 29 (twenty-nine)

ACTIVITIES:

1.   Do Worksheet 14.

Read the directions.

When the children have finished, allow time for each child to explain his picture.

Let the children write a few sentences about their picture in their tablets.

2.   Do Worksheet 15.

Have the children keep a record of the number of sit-ups they can do the first time and how many they can do after a week or two of regular exercising. Worksheet 14 can be used as a chart to keep the record.

3.   Have the children learn or invent a new exercise to teach to the class. They may be included as part of the regular exercise program.

Name _____

Draw a picture of yourself exercising.

Science 106
Worksheet 14
with page 29

Teacher check _____
Initial   Date

Name _____

My Sit-up Chart

Day	Number of Sit-ups	Day	Number of Sit-ups

Science 106
Worksheet 15
with page 29

Teacher check _____
Initial   Date

Page 30: Activity Page

VOCABULARY: build, (healthy)

MATERIALS NEEDED: pencils, crayons, Worksheet 16

TEACHING PAGE 30:

Tell the children that this page will help them to recall some of the things they have learned in the last section.

Have a volunteer find and read the three directions. Be sure the children understand what they are to do.

Let them complete the page independently.

Check together. Use as a review for the test.

ACTIVITY:

Do Worksheet 16.
Read the directions.
Let the children do the page independently.
Check together as a review.

Write yes or no.

Can you run fast? _yes_

Can you jump high? _yes_

Can you walk slowly? _yes_

Circle the words in the puzzle.

Color the words yellow.

body		build		food	
b	u	i	l	d	a
o	n	d	s	t	c
d	t	f	o	o	d
y	n	m	p	s	y

page 30 (thirty)

Name _____

Write the name of the special exercise.

jumping jacks	pushups
sit-ups	toe-touches

pushups   sit-ups

toe-touches

jumping jacks

Science 106
Worksheet 16
with page 30

Teacher check _____
Initial   Date

Page 31: Activity Page

MATERIALS NEEDED: pencils

TEACHING PAGE 31:

This page reviews some of the important concepts from the LIFEPAC. Before assigning the page, spend some time reviewing the vocabulary.

Ask the children to do such activities with the words.

Examples: Find the words that name things that grow. Find words that name foods you eat. Find words that tell what your body needs to grow strong and healthy.

Read the direction or have a student read it aloud. Go over the words in the word box and the sentences if necessary.

Have the children complete the page independently. Check it together.

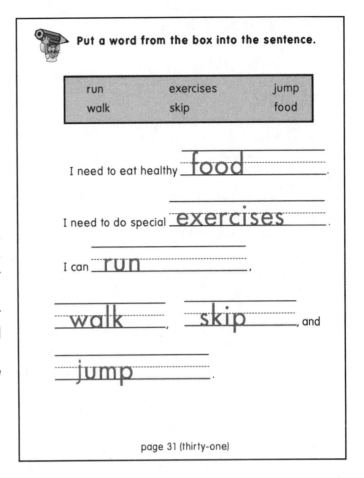

Put a word from the box into the sentence.

run	exercises	jump
walk	skip	food

I need to eat healthy food.

I need to do special exercises.

I can run,

walk, skip, and

jump.

page 31 (thirty-one)

Pages 32 and 33: Self Test 3

CONCEPT: evaluation

OBJECTIVES:

I can name three things that grow.
I can tell two ways that I am growing.
I can name five foods that are good for me.
I can show two exercises that are good for me.
I can tell how much sleep I need.

READING INTEGRATION: following directions, recalling details

VOCABULARY: Review all vocabulary.

MATERIALS NEEDED: pencils, Worksheets 17 and 18

TEACHING PAGES 32 and 33:

Review the vocabulary and concepts for the entire LIFEPAC, with special emphasis on section three.

Read through the directions for the self test with the group. Answer any questions they might have.

The general proficiency of your group will dictate whether you choose to direct the self test or allow the children to proceed independently, once directions are given.

In either case, you should be available to answer questions and to help with vocabulary, as needed.

Check at once. Review any concepts missed.

For those children who need extra help, have them work with a classroom helper or a parent to prepare for the LIFEPAC Test.

ACTIVITY:

Do Worksheets 17 and 18.
All necessary materials and instructions are listed on the Worksheets.

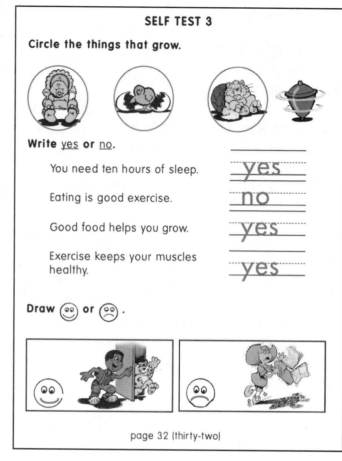

page 32 (thirty-two)

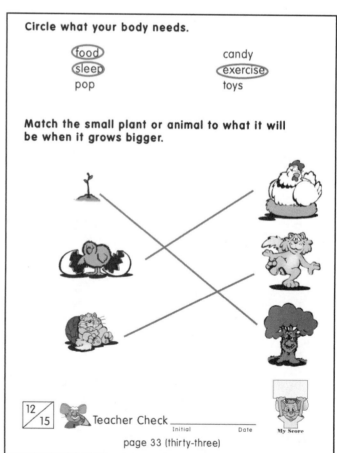

page 33 (thirty-three)

Name _____

Make a mobile to hang in your room.

You need:

crayons
scissors
glue
3 sticks or a coat hanger

colored paper or
cardboard
string

Color the pictures on Worksheet 18.
Cut out the pieces on Worksheet 18.
Glue them to paper or cardboard.
Put string through the holes.
Tie string to sticks or coat hanger.

Hang it in your room.

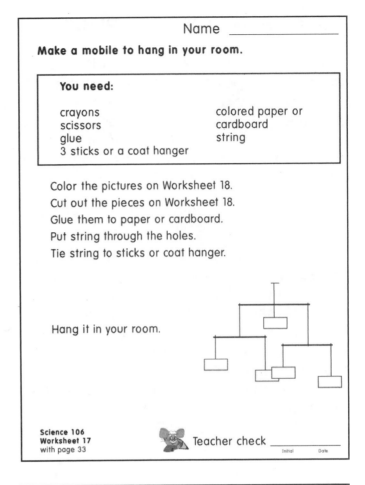

Science 106
Worksheet 17
with page 33

Teacher check _____
                Initial   Date

Name _____

BUILDING
A BETTER
BODY

GOOD
FOOD

ENOUGH SLEEP

EXERCISE

Science 106
Worksheet 18
with page 33

Teacher check _____
                Initial   Date

LIFEPAC TEST AND ALTERNATE LIFEPAC TEST:

Administer the test to the class as a group. Ask to have directions read or read them to the class. In either case, be sure that the children clearly understand. Put examples on the board if it seems necessary. Give ample time for each activity to be completed before going on to the next.

Correct immediately and discuss with the child.

Review any concepts that have been missed.

Give those children who do not achieve the 80% score additional copies of the worksheets and a list of vocabulary words to study. A parent or a classroom helper should help in the review.

When the child is ready, give the Alternate LIFEPAC Test. Use the same procedure as for the LIFEPAC TEST.

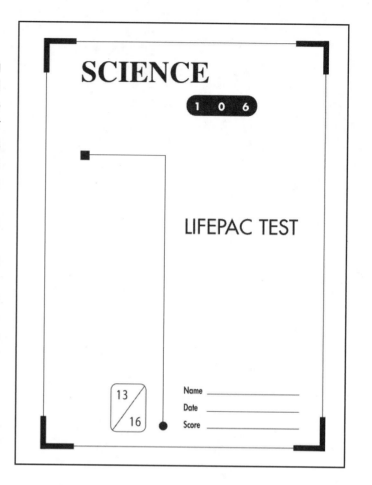

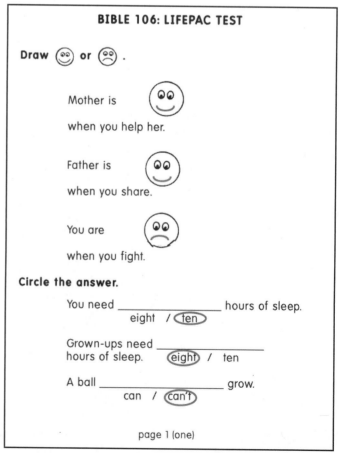

Write the word.

grow	body	eat	food

Good _food_ helps you grow.

Plants and animals _grow_ .

You _eat_ three meals every day.

Your _body_ needs food, sleep, and exercise.

Circle the healthy foods.

page 2 (two)

NOTES

page 3 (three)

SCIENCE

1 0 6

ALTERNATE
LIFEPAC TEST

14 / 17

Name _____

Date _____

Score _____

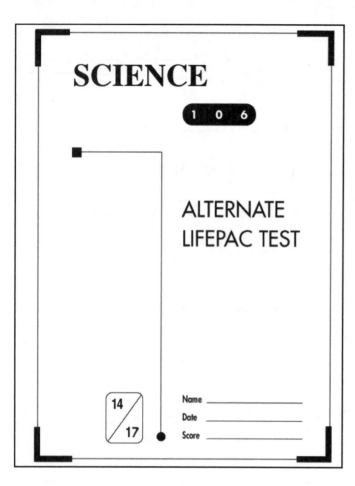

SCIENCE 106: ALTERNATE LIFEPAC TEST

Circle the things that can grow.

Write the answer.

man	cat	plant

Dan will grow to be a ___man___ .

Tat will grow to be a ___cat___ .

A seed will grow to be a ___plant___ .

Draw 😊 **or** ☹ .

page 1 (one)

Circle the answer.

How many hours should you sleep?

2   5   8   ⑩

Circle the good foods.

Write the words.

exercise	muscles

Running and jumping are good

___exercise___ .

Exercise keeps your ___muscles___ healthy.

page 2 (two)

NOTES

page 3 (three)

Page 1: God's Beautiful World

CONCEPTS: God created the world. It is filled with many places. Each place has its own kind of plants and animals.

OBJECTIVE: To introduce all the objectives.

BIBLE REFERENCE: Genesis 1

PROCESS: observing

READING INTEGRATION: listening

VOCABULARY: climate, earth, heaven

MATERIALS NEEDED: pencils; LIFEPAC Tablets; pictures of different climates, land forms, regions

TEACHING PAGE 1:

Review the creation as described in Genesis 1. Tell the children that in LIFEPAC 107 they will learn about the many lands to be found upon the earth.

Read the title and the introductory paragraphs to the class or have them read by volunteers. Discuss each paragraph with the class. Repeat the same procedure with the objectives, reminding the children that these are things they will know when the LIFEPAC is completed.

ACTIVITY:

In the Tablets the children should write the verse (Genesis 1:1) "In the beginning God created the heaven and earth."

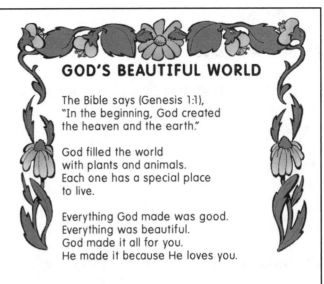

GOD'S BEAUTIFUL WORLD

The Bible says (Genesis 1:1),
"In the beginning, God created the heaven and the earth."

God filled the world with plants and animals. Each one has a special place to live.

Everything God made was good.
Everything was beautiful.
God made it all for you.
He made it because He loves you.

1. I can tell about different kinds of land.
2. I can tell about different bodies of water.
3. I can tell about different weather.

page 1 (one)

I. PART ONE

Page 2: The Land

CONCEPTS: The lands of the earth are different. People have used the lands in different ways.

OBJECTIVE: I can tell about different kinds of land.

PROCESS: observing

READING INTEGRATION: rhyming, listening, main idea

VOCABULARY: grasslands, woodlands, cities, land, (farms, deserts, mountains)

MATERIALS NEEDED: materials from your area (rocks, plants, pictures, and so on), pictures for vocabulary words

I. THE LAND

The place you live is special.
God made it just that way.
He made the plants and animals
That you see every day.

Do you live in a desert?
Or very near the sea?
Are the grasslands home to you?
Or a mountain community?

Men have built the cities
And farms upon the land.
The place you live is special.
It's just what God has planned.

page 2 (two)

TEACHING PAGE 2:

The first section of the LIFEPAC is about land. It will give some basic information about deserts, mountains, woodlands, and grasslands. The children will learn about some of the plants and animals that live in those areas.

Introduce the vocabulary words and match them to the pictures.

Read the poem to and with the class.

Have the children clap the rhythm and identify the rhyming words and the vocabulary words.

ACTIVITIES:

1. Begin a continuing class project about the region where you live. Your local Chamber of Commerce, banks, power companies, and so on, may have materials to offer. Plan a field trip to local points of interest (a botanical garden, a local park, and so on) where the children may observe the kind of place they live.

2. Write a class experience story about your visit. Have the children dictate sentences. Copy them on a chart or the chalkboard. Illustrate the story with photos taken on the field trip or by children's drawing.

Page 3: Activity Page

VOCABULARY: seashore

MATERIALS NEEDED: Worksheet 1, pencils, LIFEPAC Tablet

TEACHING PAGE 3:
Review the vocabulary from pages 1 and 2.

Show the pictures of the various land forms and climates. Have the children pay attention to the plant life.

Ask: "Which of these is the most like the land nearby?"

Read or have a child read the directions for the page.

Have a volunteer tell which answer should be circled for the first direction.

Discuss what makes the answer right.

When the directions are all understood have the children complete the page independently.

ACTIVITIES:
1. Continue the study of your local area.
2. Do Worksheet 1.

Read through the directions with the class. Help with spelling. When the Worksheet is complete give the children a chance to read their stories aloud.

3. If the practice would be appropriate, have the children copy the story (Worksheet 1) in the Tablet.

4. Set up a table for independent reading with as many books as you can find about the land forms to be studied. Include some on the plants and animals to be found in each region and on the ways people use the land.

Circle the kind of place where you live.

woodland   desert

grassland   mountains

seashore

Draw your special place to live.

Finish the sentence. Write the sentence in your Tablet.

I live in the _____ .

page 3 (three)

Name _____

Complete each sentence.

I live in _____ .
            your state

My state is in the _____ .
                    region

One animal that lives here is the _____ .

A plant that grows here is the _____ .

Science: 107
Worksheet 1
with page 3

Teacher check _____
                Initial   Date

Pages 4 and 5: Woodlands

CONCEPTS: Deer live in the woodlands. People use the woodlands.

OBJECTIVE: I can tell about different kinds of land.

PROCESSES: observing, classifying

READING INTEGRATION: recalling detail, following directions

VOCABULARY: woods, useful, (deer, bushes)

MATERIALS NEEDED: objects made from wood (paper/ pencils, and so on), picture of forest, Worksheet 2, pencils, crayons

TEACHING PAGES 4 and 5:

Tell the children that the next two pages will help them learn something about woodland regions. They will learn about some plants and animals that live there.

Ask:

"What kind of animal do you see on page 4?"

"Can you find the baby?"

"What do you call a baby deer?" (fawn) Read the paragraphs aloud.

Have the children read along with you as you repeat it.

Ask volunteers to identify the vocabulary words.

Ask:

"What do the paragraphs tell you about the woodlands?" (cool, dark, etc.)

"Why does Dorrie Deer feel safe in the woods?"

"What kind of plants would you see in the woods?" (trees, bushes.)

Provide discussion time. Use the *following questions:*

"Why do people need trees?"

"What do you use in school that is made from trees?" (desk, pencil, paper)

WOODLANDS

"I'm Dorrie Deer.
My home is cool and dark.
I live in the woods.
The trees are tall.
My baby can hide in the bushes.
Can you find him?"

"We are safe in the woods.
Baby deer can hide.
I can run fast."

page 4 (four)

Woodlands are good for people.
People use the trees.

Put an X on each way a tree is useful.

page 5 (five)

"What do you use at home that is made from trees?" (furniture, wooden spoon, the house itself perhaps)

Wood is often used as a fuel. It is used today mainly in fireplaces. It used to be used in kitchen stoves. The charcoal used in grills is a product of wood, too.

Have a child read the introductory sentences and the direction on page 5. Have the vocabulary word identified.

When the children have chosen the ways a tree is useful, discuss the reasons the paper, logs, and the wood house were chosen.

ACTIVITIES:

1. To extend the concept, have the children find out (from books, parents, or other sources) some other animals that might live in the woodlands. They might make a poster, a collage, a diorama (shoe box scene) of the woodlands including some animals to be seen

2. Do Worksheet 2.
Read the directions. Let the children do the Worksheet independently. Help the children who have difficulty with numerals over 10.
Check. Help with the spelling of animal names.
Have the children color the picture.

3. If you live in a woodland region, a lumber or paper mill may welcome a class visit.

4. Make a class poster, collage, or chart of the products of wood.

5. Extend the concept of man's use of woodlands. Early settlers depended upon meat from the animals they could trap or shoot. Homes and fences were built from the trees. Cleared land was and still is farmed. The soil in woodland areas is usually very fertile.

Name _____

Follow the dots to see another woodland animal.

I am a _____ skunk _____.

Science: 107
Worksheet 2
with page 5

Teacher check _____
Initial   Date

71

Pages 6 and 7: Deserts

CONCEPTS: Roadrunners, lizards, and snakes all live in the hot, dry, desert. Cactus is a plant that lives in the desert.

OBJECTIVE: I can tell about different kinds of land.

PROCESSES: observing, classifying

READING INTEGRATION: recalling details, irregular plurals, compound words

VOCABULARY: cactus (cacti), roadrunner, snake, lizard

MATERIALS NEEDED: pictures of the desert, desert animals, and desert plants; construction paper; Worksheets 3 and 4

TEACHING PAGES 6 and 7:

Tell the children that the next three pages will help them learn something about desert regions. They will learn about some plants and animals that live there.

"Can you name the animals in the picture on page 6?"

"Can you name the place where they live?"

Have the children read the paragraphs and tell something they learned about the desert.

Ask:

"What can a roadrunner catch?"

"What would the roadrunner do with the lizard or the snake?"

Display the cactus pictures. Discuss how God created them to be specially suited to the desert (they can store water).

Have a volunteer read the introductory paragraphs on page.

Call attention to the irregular plural of cactus, cacti (cacti) which is still more commonly used than the regularized cactuses.

Use the plural form in a sentence.

DESERTS

"Hi, boys and girls.
I'm Reddy Roadrunner.
God made me to live
in the desert.
The desert is hot.
It is very dry."

"I have long legs.
They help me run fast.
I can catch lizards.
Sometimes I catch snakes."

page 6 (six)

God made a special kind of plant for the desert. It is called a cactus.

A cactus can store water.
It does not need much rain.
A cactus can be very tall.
Some cacti are small.

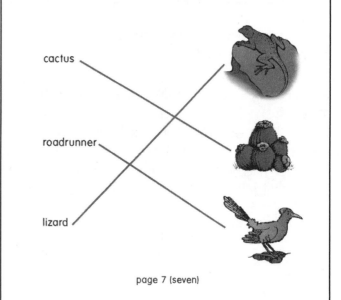

cactus

roadrunner

lizard

page 7 (seven)

Example:

All cacti can store water.

Have the children find the compound word (roadrunner) on the page. Ask a volunteer to read the word and tell the two words it contains.

Have a volunteer read the direction sentence. Let the children complete the activity. Check the answers.

ACTIVITIES:

1. Do Worksheet 3.
Read the direction. Provide pictures of each type of cactus, if possible, for the children to use as a guide.

2. Art project: Provide 9" x 12" construction paper, thin tempera paint (orange), brushes, black construction paper, scissors, and glue.

Paint a thin wash of orange tempera over the construction paper. Leave streaks horizontally across the 12 inch length as a brilliant sunset.

Cut an irregular ground and cactus shapes out of the black paper. Glue onto the orange washed construction paper. The result will be a desert scene silhouetted against a sunset.

3. To extend the concept, have the children find out (from books, parents, or other sources) some other animals that might live in the desert. They could make a poster, collage, or a diorama of the desert, including typical plants or animals.

4. Do Worksheet 4.

Have volunteers read the sentences: Some people like to live in the desert. The desert is sunny and warm.

Ask:

"What kinds of things could people do in the desert to enjoy the out-of-doors?" (hiking, camping, swimming, horseback riding)

"Since it is hot and dry in the desert, what would people need to live there?" (water)

"Where would the water come from?" (deep wells, irrigation from rivers, water storage in reservoirs-dammed up rivers)

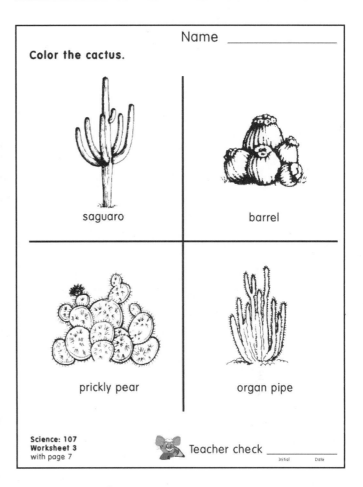

Name _____

Color the cactus.

saguaro

barrel

prickly pear

organ pipe

Science: 107
Worksheet 3
with page 7

Teacher check _____
Initial   Date

Have a child read: Farmers can grow crops all year.

Discuss how year round warm weather is good for farming.

Some of the farm products of irrigated desert lands are citrus, fruits, olives, pecans, cotton, and some grains. People of the desert can grow foods for their families all year round if there is enough water.

Have the children do the activity in their Tablets.

5. Make a collage of the products of cotton or other things grown on a desert farm.

6. Have the children read the sentences from their Tablet done for Worksheet 4.

Name _____

Some people like to live in the desert.

The desert is sunny and warm.

Farmers can grow crops all year.

Color the pictures.
Write a sentence about the desert in your Tablet.

Science: 107
Worksheet 4
with page 7

Teacher check _____
　　　　　　　　　　Initial　　　Date

Page 8: Grasslands

CONCEPT: Grasslands are good farmlands.

OBJECTIVE: I can tell about different kinds of land.

PROCESS: observing.

READING INTEGRATION: main idea, listening, compound words

VOCABULARY: prairie, (grasslands)

MATERIALS NEEDED: pictures of grasslands, Worksheet 5, pencils, crayons

TEACHING PAGE 8:
Tell the children that this page and the next one will help them learn something about grassland regions and the plants and animals that live there.
Ask:
"What kind of animal do you see on page 8?"
"Can you tell something about the place where the prairie dog lives?"
Read the sentences to the class. Ask someone to find the name of the animal (prairie dog). Have another child identify the name of the region where the prairie dog lives (grassland: compound word; synonym for prairie).
Ask:
"How do people use the grasslands?"

ACTIVITIES:
1. To extend the concept, have the children find out (from books, parents, or other sources) some other animals that might live in the grasslands. They might make a poster, a collage, or a diorama of the grasslands including some animals to be found there.
2. Do Worksheet 5.
Read the directions.
Let the children do the page independently.

GRASSLANDS

"I am Petey Prairie Dog.
I live in the grasslands.
I can sit in my town and
see a long way."

Grasslands are very flat or rolling.
Farmers grow corn and wheat.
Some farmers have pigs.
Other farmers raise cattle.

page 8 (eight)

Help with the spelling of *buffalo*.
Check together and talk about other prairie animals.
Have the children color the picture.

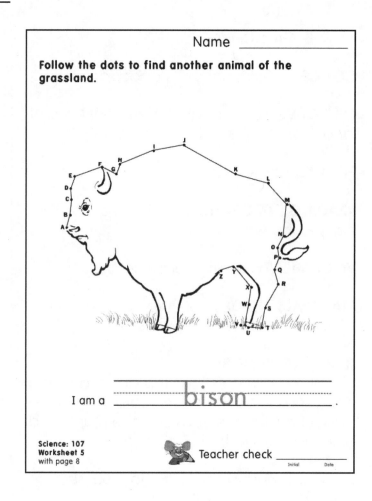

Name _____

Follow the dots to find another animal of the grassland.

I am a _____ bison _____.

Science: 107
Worksheet 5
with page 8

Teacher check _____
Initial   Date

76

Page 9: Activity Page

MATERIALS NEEDED: pencils, LIFEPAC Tablet

TEACHING PAGE 9:

Provide a short review of the vocabulary words presented so far in the LIFEPAC.

Review the things they have learned so far about woodlands, desert, and grasslands. For example you might ask: "Who can tell me the name of an animal that lives in the desert?" "Which region has tall trees?" "Which area is best for farming?"

Be sure the children understand the directions. Let them complete this page independently. Check it together. The children should be able to tell why they chose each answer.

ACTIVITIES:

1. In a discovery center or art center, provide flat boxes of sand and materials children might use to make models of each land region. They should include plants, animals, and ways people use the land. Some materials (construction paper, toothpicks, popsicle sticks, and so on) might be included.

2. Have the children write two paragraphs about the region that sounds most interesting to them.

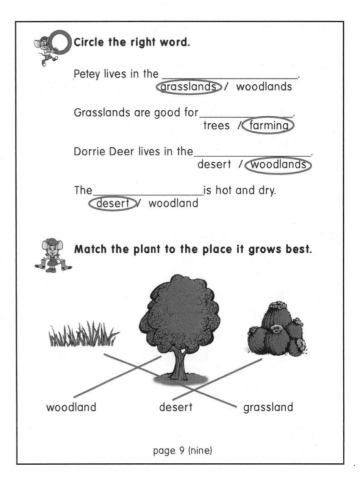

Circle the right word.

Petey lives in the _____.
grasslands / woodlands

Grasslands are good for_____.
trees / farming

Dorrie Deer lives in the_____.
desert / woodlands

The_____is hot and dry.
desert / woodland

Match the plant to the place it grows best.

woodland   desert   grassland

page 9 (nine)

Pages 10 and 11: Mountains

CONCEPTS: Mountains are rocky and cool. Mountains are divided by valleys where the animals can find grass to eat.

OBJECTIVE: I can tell about different kinds of land.

PROCESS: observing

READING INTEGRATION: main idea, recalling details, plurals

VOCABULARY: goat, valley, mountain

MATERIALS NEEDED: pictures of mountain regions (plants, animals, formations, and so on)

TEACHING PAGES 10 and 11:

Tell the children that the next few pages will help them learn something about mountain regions. They will learn about some plants and animals that live there.

Have a child read the paragraph, or read it to the group.

Ask the children to identify the vocabulary words and to tell something they can learn about mountains from what they read in the paragraph.

You might ask these questions to promote recall:

"What kind of animal is Max?" "Is it hot in the mountains?"

"What are mountains made of?" *Note:* that page 11 will help them learn more about mountains. Introduce the word valley. On the picture of mountains point out where the valleys are found (between the mountains). Have the children notice that very often mountains are covered by forests, except for the highest peaks. The mountain goat climbs high above the forests and comes back down to eat and to find shelter when the weather is bad.

MOUNTAINS

"I'm Max Mountain Goat.
I live high on a mountain.
It is a tall mountain.
It is cold where I live.
God gave me a warm coat.
My mountain is made of rock.
I like to jump and run.
I jump from rock to rock.

page 10 (ten)

"Sometimes, I go down the mountain—down, down to the valley. I go down to eat. Sweet grass grows in the valley. I eat and eat."

Circle the right word.

goat / goats   animal / animals

mountain / mountains   rock / rocks

page 11 (eleven)

Have a volunteer read the paragraph.
Ask:
"Where does Max go to eat?"
"What grows in the valleys?"
Tell the class that the exercise will help them to remember when to add s to a word when it means more than one.

Have a child read the direction. Let the children complete the page independently. Check it together.

ACTIVITIES:

1. To extend the concept, have the children find out (from books, parents, or other sources) some other animals or plants that live in the mountains. They could make a poster, collage, or a diorama of animals and plants to be found there.

2. Include mountains in the "sandbox" model projects.

3. If you live in a mountain community, a field trip to a mountain park, a mine, or other point of interest would be appropriate.

Page 12: Mountains

CONCEPT: People use mountain regions for work and for play.

OBJECTIVE: I can tell about different kinds of land.

PROCESS: observing

READING INTEGRATION: recalling details

VOCABULARY: community

MATERIALS NEEDED: pencils, LIFEPAC Tablet, Worksheet 6, crayons

TEACHING PAGE 12:

Introduce the word community. Tell the children that a community can be a neighborhood in a large city; it can be a town or a village; or it can be just a group of people who live fairly close together.

Tell the children that this page will help them learn how people use mountain lands.

Read the introductory sentences.

Discuss each picture.

Mining:

"What do people get out of a mine?" (coal, copper, gold, silver)

"What tools might a miner use?"

Fishing:

"Do people fish for fun or for work?"

"Could you catch a whale in a mountain stream?"

Skiing:

Tell how once people skied to get from one place to another. Fur trappers wore skis or snowshoes to check their traps. Early settlers used skis to go to the trading post (store) for supplies. Ask: "Why do people ski today?" (fun, good exercise)

Have the children read and do the final activity.

ACTIVITY:

Do Worksheet 6

People live in mountain communities. Here are some things they do.

Mining | Fishing

Skiing

Write this sentence in your tablet.

Thank you, God, for the beautiful mountains.

page 12 (twelve)

Discuss each illustration as a review of section one. Discuss the four regional words the children have learned.

Read the directions. Let the children complete the sheet independently.

Check together. Review anything the children still do not comprehend.

Name _____

Section I: Review

Color the pictures. Write the word.

| mountains | grasslands |
| woodlands | desert |

woodlands    mountains

desert    grasslands

Science: 107
Worksheet 6
with page 12

Teacher check _____
Initial   Date

Page 13: Activity Page

MATERIALS NEEDED: crayons, LIFEPAC Tablet, pencils

TEACHING PAGE 13:

Read the directions. Discuss some things that people may like to do in the mountains (hike, camp, fish, ski, hunt, and so on).

Instruct the children to draw and color their pictures and to write two or three paragraphs about in their Tablets.

Allow time (a day or two) for the children to read their paragraphs and talk about their pictures. Review the correct speaking procedures from the Language Arts LIFEPACs.

Draw a picture of what you would like to do in the mountains.

Teacher Check _____
                Initial   Date
page 13 (thirteen)

Pages 14 and 15: Self Test

CONCEPT: evaluation

OBJECTIVE: I can tell about different kinds of land.

READING INTEGRATION: main idea, recalling details, following written directions

VOCABULARY: Review all the vocabulary words.

MATERIALS NEEDED: pencils, Worksheet

TEACHING PAGES 14 and 15:
Review the vocabulary words.

Practice matching regions to animals, plants, and the ways people use the land.

Read all the directions with the children. Be sure they are understood.

The general proficiency of your group should dictate whether you choose to direct the self test or allow the children to proceed independently, once directions are given.

In either case you should be available to answer questions and to help with the vocabulary as needed.

ACTIVITIES:
1.   Do Worksheet 7.

Read the directions. Once the children understand what they are to do, let them complete the page independently. Caution them to trace each path first with their finger until they are sure they have the right one.

Check together. Use discussion as a review of section one concepts.

2.   Complete the class projects (sandbox models and displays).

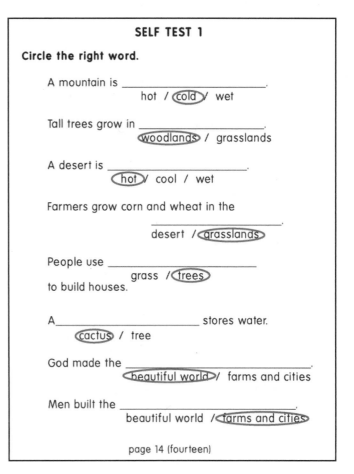

SELF TEST 1

Circle the right word.

A mountain is _____.
hot / cold / wet

Tall trees grow in _____.
woodlands / grasslands

A desert is _____.
hot / cool / wet

Farmers grow corn and wheat in the _____.
desert / grasslands

People use _____
grass / trees
to build houses.

A_____ stores water.
cactus / tree

God made the _____.
beautiful world / farms and cities

Men built the _____.
beautiful world / farms and cities

page 14 (fourteen)

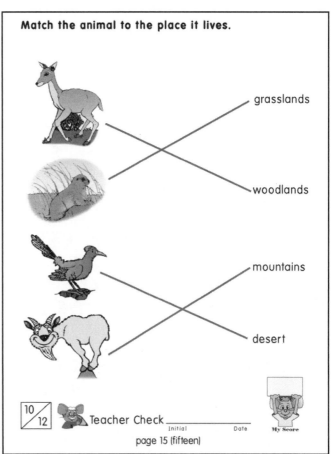

Match the animal to the place it lives.

grasslands

woodlands

mountains

desert

10/12   Teacher Check _____
Initial   Date

page 15 (fifteen)

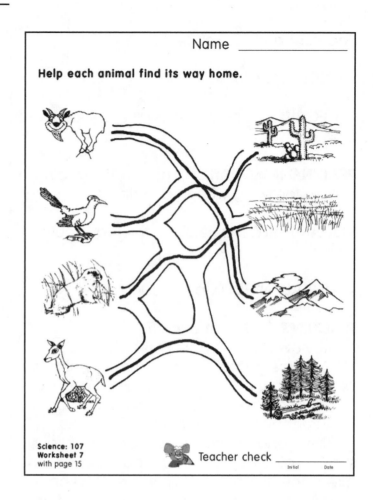

Name _____

Help each animal find its way home.

Science: 107
Worksheet 7
with page 15

Teacher check _____
Initial   Date

II. PART TWO

Page 16: The Water

CONCEPTS: Water is necessary for life. Water can be found in many places.

OBJECTIVE:
I can tell about different bodies of water.

PROCESS: observing

READING INTEGRATION: main idea

VOCABULARY: living, ocean, lakes, rivers, (water)

MATERIALS NEEDED: pictures of different bodies of water (oceans, lakes, rivers, streams, and so on), LIFEPAC Tablet, pencils

TEACHING PAGE 16:

Introduce the section by showing the pictures. Ask the children what they see in all the pictures (water).

Display the pictures identified with the word cards: ocean, lakes, and rivers.

Ask the children what living thing they see in the pictures. By now they should know that the plants are living things as well as the animals.

Read the paragraph together or have children take turns.

Ask:

"Who needs water?" (people, animals, plants)

"Where is water?"

"Who can find a prayer in the paragraph?" Read it aloud.

ACTIVITIES:

1. If you are in a community near a body of water, plan a field trip to visit a point of interest nearby: an oceanarium, a dam, a shipyard, a beach, a park, or other place. Have the children use their ears, eyes, and other senses to learn about the place you visit.

II. THE WATER

All living things need water.
People need water.
Animals need water.
Plants need water.
Water is on the earth.
Water is in the sky.
Thank you, God,
for giving us water.

page 16 (sixteen)

2. After the field trip write a class experience story about the place you visit.

Have the children dictate sentences about what they observed.

Write the sentences on the chalkboard or on chart paper.

If the children are able, have them copy the experience story in their Tablets or write an experience story of their own.

3. You may wish to take pictures to illustrate the experience story or have the children draw, paint or color pictures to illustrate it.

Page 17: Activity Page

MATERIALS NEEDED: crayons, pencils, LIFEPAC Tablet

TEACHING PAGE 17:

Review the important idea from page 16. "All living things need water."

Call attention to the three icons.

Ask what the icons mean. (They are a sign that means the child has something to do.)

Ask for a volunteer to read the direction next to the icons.

Be sure all the children understand what they are to do.

Let them complete the page independently. Check together.

ACTIVITY:

Set up a table for independent reading with as many books as you can about bodies of water and the plants and animals that live in and near them.

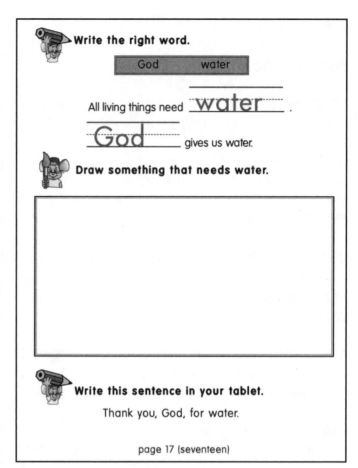

Write the right word.

God   water

All living things need water .

God gives us water.

Draw something that needs water.

Write this sentence in your tablet.

Thank you, God, for water.

page 17 (seventeen)

Page 18 : Oceans

CONCEPT: the ocean

OBJECTIVE: I can tell about different bodies of water.

PROCESSES: observing, comparing

READING INTEGRATION: main idea, recalling details

VOCABULARY: dolphin, fish, gills, breathe, (ocean, salty)

MATERIALS NEEDED: pictures of ocean animals and plants, Worksheet 8, pencils, crayons

TEACHING PAGE 18 :

Tell the children that this page and the next are about the oceans. They will learn about some plants and animals that live there.

Teach the vocabulary.

Ask:

"What kind of animal do you see on page 18?" (dolphin)

Note: If the children call the dolphin a fish tell them that even though it looks like a fish it is really a mammal. (It feeds milk to its young). Whales are mammals, too.

Have the children read in turn the information about the ocean.

Promote discussion about the sentences.

Discussion questions: "What sense would you use to discover that ocean water is salty?"

"What kind of plants might live in the ocean?"

"What other animals live in the ocean?" (If you live near the ocean your children may have quite a bit of information about this.)

Ask for volunteers to tell something they learned from this page.

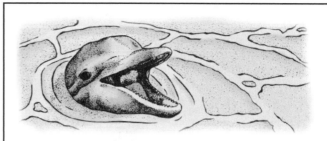

OCEANS

Oceans are big.
Ocean water is salty.
Animals live in the ocean.
Plants live in the ocean.
Dazy Dolphin lives in the ocean.
"I can swim fast," says Dazy.
"I can jump and dive.
The ocean is deep.
Sometimes I dive to the bottom.
I come up again.
I need air, like you.
My friends, the fish,
do not need air.
God gave them gills.
Gills help them breathe
underwater."

page 18 (eighteen)

ACTIVITIES:

1. To extend the concept, have the children find out (from books, parents, or other sources) some other facts about the ocean. They might make a collage, diorama, or poster about the ocean.

2. Do Worksheet 8.

Read the directions. Review the words in the box. Let the children do the sheet independently. Help with vocabulary if necessary. Check together.

Name _____

Write the words.

dolphin	ocean
gills	salty

Ocean water is _____ salty _____ .

Dazy is a _____ dolphin _____ .

Fish have _____ gills _____ .

An _____ ocean _____ is very big.

Draw a picture of a fish.

Science: 107
Worksheet 8
with page 18

Teacher check _____
Initial   Date

Page 19: Activity Page

MATERIALS NEEDED: pencils, crayons, LIFEPAC Tablet

TEACHING PAGE 19:

Tell the children that this picture shows some living things in the ocean. Use available books to identify some of them.

Ask a volunteer to read the directions and have the children complete the page.

When it is completed ask what animal appeared when they connected the dots (dolphin).

ACTIVITY:

Have the children write a sentence about the picture on page 19 in their Tablets.

Those who are able may be allowed to write a story (two or more paragraphs) about one of the animals.

Follow the dots. Color the picture.

page 19 (nineteen)

Pages 20 and 21: Seashore

CONCEPTS: The seashore is different from other kinds of land. Its plants and animals need the salty water to live.

OBJECTIVES: I can tell about different kinds of land.

I can tell about different bodies of water.

PROCESS: observing

READING INTEGRATION: recalling detail, compound words, synonym

VOCABULARY: starfish, sandy, (seashore)

MATERIALS NEEDED: pictures of seashore with birds and animals, Worksheet 9, crayons

TEACHING PAGES 20 and 21:

Tell the children that the next two pages are about land along the ocean. This land is wet and sandy. It is called the seashore.

Display the vocabulary words. Identify them for the children if necessary. Ask which two are compound words. Have volunteers tell the words for each (sea/shore, star/fish). Tell them that sea is another name for ocean.

Have the children read in turn the sentences about the seashore.

SEASHORE

Sometimes the seashore is wet.
Sometimes it is dry.
The land is sandy.
Stan Starfish lives
near the seashore.
"I live in the water," says Stan.
"I must move
when the water moves.
Without water
I could not live."

page 20 (twenty)

Other seashore animals cannot live <u>in</u> the water.

Sea birds find food in the water.

People find food in the water, too.

 Circle <u>yes</u> **or** <u>no</u>.

A starfish lives in the water.
yes / no

A sea bird lives in the water.
yes / no

People live in the water.
yes / no

A dolphin lives in the water.
yes / no

page 21 (twenty-one)

Promote discussion about the sentences.

Note: The sand is wet and dry as the tide moves in and out. High tide covers much of the seashore. Low tide exposes more sand and rock along the shore. The tide comes in and out twice each day. *Discussion questions:*

"What animal moves with the water?" (page 20)

"What animals find food in the water?" (page 21)

"What kind of food can people find in the water?" (page 21)

Tell what you know about the seashore.

Have the children complete the activity on page 21. Read the sentences if necessary.

ACTIVITY:

Do Worksheet 9.

Before the worksheets are distributed, discuss other ways people use the seashore.

Examples: *Vacation fun, surfing,*
swimming, fishing,
boating, building
sandcastles,
Transportation, ships,
large and small

Distribute the worksheets. Let the children color the picture after you have discussed it with them.

Name _____

Fun at the Seashore
- a picture to color -

Science: 107
Worksheet 9
with page 21

Teacher check _____
Initial   Date

Page 22: Lakes

CONCEPTS: Lakes have fresh water. They are home to many plants and animals.

OBJECTIVE:
I can tell about different bodies of water.

PROCESSES: observing, comparing

READING INTEGRATION:
main idea, recalling details

VOCABULARY: turtle (lake)

MATERIALS NEEDED: pictures of lakes and the fish, plants, and animals that live in or near a lake (frogs, otters, reeds, water lilies, and so on); Worksheet 10; pencils; crayons; LIFEPAC Tablet

LAKES

"My name is Snappy Turtle.
God made me.
I live by a lake.
The lake is not salty.
Plants grow in the lake.
Fish swim in the lake.
Other animals live near the shore.
People live near the lake, too."

page 22 (twenty-two)

TEACHING PAGE 22:
Tell the children that this page will help them learn some things about lakes and how they are different from oceans.

Ask the children to identify the animal in the picture on page 22 (turtle).

Read the information sentences with the children. Discuss the ideas they introduce.
Discussion questions:
"Where does Snappy live?"
"How is a lake different from the ocean?"
"What might you find in the water of a lake?"
"What might you find near the shore of a lake?"

Have the children write a sentence or two about a lake in their Tablets.

ACTIVITIES:

1. To extend the concept, have the children find out (from books, parents, or other sources) more about life around a lake. They might make a poster, collage, or diorama of life around a lake.

2. If you live in the Great Lakes area you might study transportation on the big lakes. Many raw materials (iron ore) and manufactured products are transported by water.

3. In the Great Lakes area, fishing is also an important industry. If you are near a fishing community you might arrange a visit to one of the fishermen. Write an experience story about the visit.

4. Make a mural of people enjoying themselves at a lake.

5. Do Worksheet 10.

Read the directions. When the children have completed the picture, check together and discuss other things that are fun to do at a lake (swimming, boating, picnicking, and so on).

Name _____

Fun at the Lake.

Follow the dots. Color the picture.

Science: 107
Worksheet 10
with page 22

Teacher check _____
                    Initial   Date

Page 23: Activity Page

MATERIALS NEEDED: pencils, crayons, LIFEPAC Tablet, alphabet charts

TEACHING PAGE 23:

Review the similarities and differences of oceans and lakes. Review the vocabulary words.

Have a volunteer read the directions.

Let the children complete the page independently. Check together.

Ask a volunteer to name Snappy's friend.

Write this sentence on the chalkboard. Snappy's friend is a frog. Have the children write it in their Tablets.

page 23 (twenty-three)

Page 24: Rivers

CONCEPTS: Rivers are homes for fish and animals. They provide transportation and water for people.

OBJECTIVE: I can tell about different bodies of water.

PROCESSES: observing, comparing

READING INTEGRATION: main idea, recalling detail

VOCABULARY: catfish, travel, clean, (drink, river)

MATERIALS NEEDED: pictures of rivers, wildlife around rivers, riverboats, and so on; Worksheet 11, crayons

RIVERS

"I'm Big Catfish.
I live in the river.
The river is very long.
It goes to the ocean.
The river helps people.
Big boats travel on the river.
The river gives you water to drink.
God made the river clean.
Help me keep it clean."

page 24 (twenty-four)

TEACHING PAGE 24:

This page is about rivers. It will help the children learn something about how rivers are alike and different from oceans and lakes.

Ask a volunteer to identify the animal (fish) in the picture. Tell the children that a catfish does a special job in the river. He helps to keep it clean. Many people fish for catfish. It is very good to eat.

Read the information sentences with group.

Discussion questions: "How is a river like a lake but different from the ocean?" (fresh water)

"Does every river go to the ocean?" (No. Some rivers flow into other rivers which then go to the ocean.)

"What other animals might live in or near a river?"

"How might people use rivers?"

ACTIVITIES:

1. To extend the concept, have the children find out more about rivers (from books, parents, or other sources). They might make a poster, collage, or diorama of a river scene.

2. Most parts of our country are near a river, large or small. Arrange a field trip to a nearby river. Write an experience story about your visit.

3. Do Worksheet 11.

Before you distribute the Worksheet, tell the children about the riverboats and how they are driven by big paddle wheels. Tell the children that they were used to carry products up and down the Mississippi, the longest river in our country.

Read the direction. Have the children color the picture and write a paragraph about the picture in their Tablets.

Allow time for the children to read their paragraphs in small groups or to the entire class.

Name _____

Color the riverboat.

Science: 107
Worksheet 11
with page 24

Teacher check _____

Initial   Date

Page 25: Activity Page

MATERIALS NEEDED: pencils

TEACHING PAGE 25:

This page will provide review for the self test. Spend some time with the pictures and the vocabulary words for the section.

Have a volunteer read the direction.

Let the children complete the page independently. Check it together.

ACTIVITIES:

1. Try to have all projects finished and turned in before the self test. Allow children to share or display their work.

2. Do Worksheet 12.

This worksheet may be used with page 25 or as a recheck after the self test.

Read the direction. Have the children trace each path with their finger before doing it in pencil or crayon.

Check together. Discuss each kind of water location as a review.

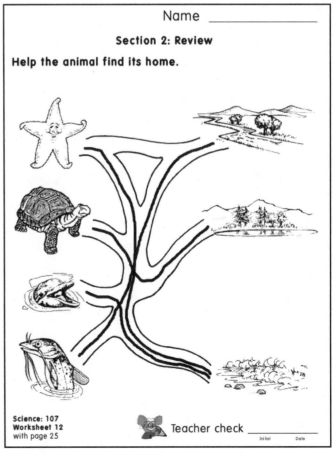

Pages 26 and 27: Self Test 2

CONCEPT: evaluation

OBJECTIVES: I can tell about different kinds of land.
I can tell about different bodies of water.

READING INTEGRATION: following directions, recalling details

VOCABULARY: Review all the vocabulary words.

MATERIALS NEEDED: pencils

TEACHING PAGES 26 and 27:
Review vocabulary and concepts for sections 1 and 2.

Practice matching the bodies of water to the plants and animals and uses of them.

Read all the directions with the children. Be sure they are understood.

The general proficiency of your group will dictate whether you choose to direct the self test or allow the children to proceed independently, once directions are given.

In either case you should be available to answer questions and to help with vocabulary, as needed.

Have the children who need the review go over the first two sections with their parents or a classroom helper. Then give the Worksheet or a similar review page as a second check.

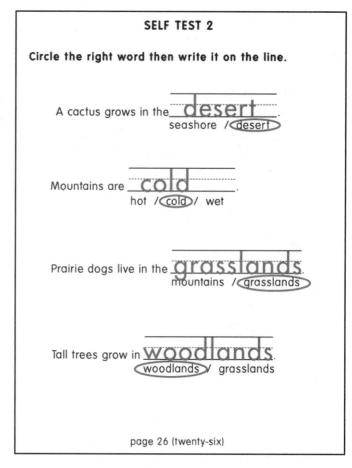

SELF TEST 2

Circle the right word then write it on the line.

A cactus grows in the ___desert___.
seashore / desert

Mountains are ___cold___.
hot / cold / wet

Prairie dogs live in the ___grasslands___.
mountains / grasslands

Tall trees grow in ___woodlands___.
woodlands / grasslands

page 26 (twenty-six)

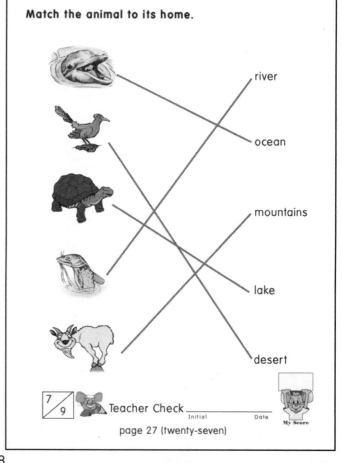

Match the animal to its home.

river

ocean

mountains

lake

desert

7/9 Teacher Check _____
Initial   Date

My Score

page 27 (twenty-seven)

III. PART THREE

Page 28: The Weather

CONCEPT: Weather includes wind, rain, snow, sunshine, and the temperature of the air.

OBJECTIVE: I can tell about different weather.

PROCESS: observing

READING INTEGRATION: recalling details, main idea

VOCABULARY: snow, sunshine, warmer, cooler, (wind, rain)

MATERIALS NEEDED: pictures of different kinds of weather

III. THE WEATHER

Weather comes from God.
God makes the wind blow.
He makes the air cooler or warmer.
God sends the rain or the snow.
He makes the sunshine.

page 28 (twenty-eight)

TEACHING PAGE 28:

Teach the vocabulary.

Have the children match the word with its corresponding picture.

Read the sentences to the group, or have them read by volunteers.

Discussion questions: "Who makes the weather?" (God)

"How does rain help?"

"How does snow help?"

"How does sunshine help?"

"How does wind help?"

"Can you think of a way these kinds of weather might cause problems?" (Examples: tornado, flood, slippery roads, sunburn)

ACTIVITY:

Construct and display a daily weather chart. Take a moment each morning to move the indicators to the weather condition for the day.

Page 29: Climate and Seasons

CONCEPT: climate and seasons

OBJECTIVE: I can tell about different weather.

PROCESS: comparing

READING INTEGRATION: rhyming, listening, recalling details

VOCABULARY: climate, seasons, summer, autumn.(weather, winter, spring)

MATERIALS NEEDED: pencils, crayons

TEACHING PAGE 29:

Tell the children that this last section is about the different climates and kinds of weather.

Introduce the vocabulary words and match them to the pictures.

Read the poem to and with the class.

Have the children clap the rhythm and identify the rhyming words and the vocabulary words.

ACTIVITY:

Set up a table for independent reading with as many books as you can find about climate, weather, and seasons.

Listen to this poem.

Climate is weather
All the year 'round.
It's sunshine and clouds
And rain falling down.

There's snow in the winter,
Spring sun's warming rays,
Sizzling summer
And crisp autumn days.

God made the world perfect.
Let's keep it that way.
So our children can love
All the seasons some day.

Draw a picture about the poem.

page 29 (twenty-nine)

Pages 30 and 31: Rain

CONCEPT: water cycle

OBJECTIVE: I can tell about different weather.

BIBLE REFERENCE: Isaiah 55:10 and 11; Ecclesiastes 1:6 and 7; Job 36:27 and 28; Isaiah 40:12.

READING INTEGRATION: main idea, recalling detail, compound words

VOCABULARY: mysterious, dew, invisible, cloud, raindrop

MATERIALS NEEDED: pencils, hot plate, pan, water, flat pan, ice cubes, Worksheet 13, LIFEPAC Tablet

TEACHING PAGES 30 and 31:

Tell the children that one of the most wonderful gifts of God is the gift of water. Water is used over and over again.

Go over the vocabulary words.

Tell the children to read the story about Mysterious Mr. Raindrop. Read it to them if it is appropriate.

Discussion questions: "Name some ways Mr. Raindrop can be found on earth." (rain, snow, dew, rivers, lakes, oceans)

"How can you see a raindrop in the sky?" (It is part of a cloud.)

"Think of some other ways you might see Mr. Raindrop?" (ice, hail, in the faucet at home)

Have a child read the sentence at the top of page 31. Ask another to read the direction.

Have the children complete the activity. Check it together.

Have a child read the direction and the prayer at the bottom of the page. Let the class write the prayer in their Tablets.

MYSTERIOUS MR. RAINDROP

Mr. Raindrop is very old.
He is always around you.
Sometimes you can see him.
Mr. Raindrop can be rain.
Mr. Raindrop can be snow.
In the morning
you see him as dew.

Sometimes,
Mr. Raindrop
is invisible.
He hides in the air.
Many raindrops may hide
together.
They become a cloud.
The clouds get bigger.
Then mysterious Mr. Raindrop
falls to earth again.

page 30 (thirty)

Mr. Raindrop can be all of these things.

Name them. Use these words.

rain   snow   cloud   dew

snow

cloud

rain

dew

Write this sentence in your Tablet.

Thank you, God, for raindrops.

page 31 (thirty-one)

ACTIVITIES:

1. Do Worksheet 13.

Read the directions. Do the first one with the children. Read the word *rain*. Ask the children to match it to a word in the first set to make a compound word (drop). Have the children trace the line. Have them trace the word *raindrop*.

Do a second word if necessary. Then let the children complete the page independently.

Check together. Have the children tell what they remember about each word.

2. Do a class experiment.

On a hot plate, boil water and have the children observe the steam rising (it is like a cloud). Hold a flat pan filled with ice cubes directly over the rising steam. The water in the steam condenses on the bottom cold pan and begins to drip off like raindrops.

3. Have your class write experience story about experiment. Have them copy it in the Tablets.

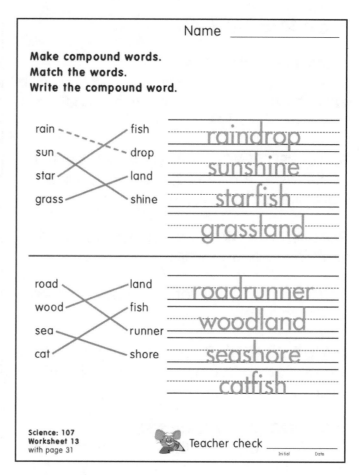

Name _____

Make compound words.
Match the words.
Write the compound word.

rain ---- fish
sun ---- drop
star ---- land
grass ---- shine

raindrop
sunshine
starfish
grassland

road ---- land
wood ---- fish
sea ---- runner
cat ---- shore

roadrunner
woodland
seashore
catfish

Science: 107
Worksheet 13
with page 31

Teacher check _____
Initial   Date

102

Pages 32 and 33: Clouds

CONCEPT: clouds signal weather

OBJECTIVE: I can tell about different weather.

PROCESS: observing

READING INTEGRATION: main idea, recalling details

VOCABULARY: sailing ships, fluffy, thin, tail (angry)

MATERIALS NEEDED: pictures of different types of clouds, crayons, LIFEPAC Tablet, pencils

TEACHING PAGES 32 and 33:

Take your class out of doors and have them observe the clouds. (Try to pick a day when there is more than one kind of cloud.)

Note: Check in an encyclopedia or a weather book to find descriptions of the types of cloud.

If you have a very capable group you might have them learn the names of some cloud formations.

Teach the vocabulary.

Have the children take turns reading the sentences about clouds.

Questions: "What can you learn by watching the clouds?"

"What color is a cloud when it's about to rain?"

Have the children draw their pictures on page 33. Have them write two paragraphs about their pictures. Allow time to discuss both their pictures and their paragraphs.

ACTIVITIES:

1. Continue daily weather reporting.
2. If possible, visit a weather reporting station and write a class experience story about it.
3. Invite a local weatherman to speak to the class about his job.

CLOUDS

Clouds are like sailing ships.
They sail across the sky.
Some clouds are white
and fluffy.
Others are thin
like a horse's tail.
Sometimes clouds look angry.
They are big and black.
Then you know
they are going to rain.

page 32 (thirty-two)

Draw a picture that you have seen in the clouds.

page 33 (thirty-three)

Pages 34 and 35: Wind

CONCEPT: We do not see the wind, but we can see what it does.

OBJECTIVE: I can tell about different weather.

PROCESS: observing

READING INTEGRATION: main idea, listening, rhyming, recalling details, following directions

MATERIALS NEEDED: crayons, Worksheet 14, pencils, banner paper, paints, brushes

TEACHING PAGES 34 and 35:

Discuss the wind. Some winds are gentle. Others can be very strong and destructive.

Have the children contribute ideas of how different winds make them feel. This page is a listening experience. The children are to listen for the main idea of the poem. (You cannot see the wind.)

Repeat it and have the children read along. Discuss the images in the poem (leaves hang trembling, trees bowing their heads).

Have a child read two direction sentences indicated by the arrows.

Let the children complete the page independently. Check it together. Let the children talk about their pictures.

ACTIVITIES:

1. Have children memorize the poem and perform it as a choral reading.

2. Do Worksheet 14.

Read the direction at the top of the Worksheet.

Make sure the children know that they are to color only those things that show the wind blowing.

Read the second direction. Let the children complete the sheet independently.

WIND
You cannot see wind,
but you can see what it does.

Who Has Seen the Wind?

Who has seen the wind?
Neither I nor you;
But when the leaves hang trembling,
The wind is passing thro'.

Who has seen the wind?
Neither you nor I;
But when the trees bow down their heads,
The wind is passing by.

by Christina Rossetti

page 34 (thirty-four)

 Circle <u>yes</u> **or** <u>no</u>.

You can see the wind.

yes / (no)

Wind can move clouds.

(yes) / no

Mr. Raindrop is sometimes wind.

yes / (no)

God sends rain and snow.

(yes) / no

 Draw a <u>windy</u> **picture.**

page 35 (thirty-five)

Check by having the children name each thing they have colored and tell how it shows the wind blowing. Have a child read the sentences and answers at the bottom.

3. Continue the weather reports.

4. Make a weather mural or set of weather posters. Provide tempera paint, brushes, and butcher paper. You might title the display: "Weather We See and Feel".

Name _____

Color the things in the picture that show the wind is blowing.

Circle <u>yes</u> **or** <u>no</u>.

The wind can move things.
yes / no

You can see the wind.
yes / no

Science: 107
Worksheet 14
with page 35

Teacher check _____
Initial   Date

Pages 36 and 37: Seasons

CONCEPTS: A year has four seasons. No matter where you live the weather conditions change with the seasons.

OBJECTIVES: I can tell about different weather.

PROCESSES: observing, ordering

READING INTEGRATION: rhyming, recalling details, sequencing

VOCABULARY: (season, summer, winter, autumn, spring)

MATERIALS NEEDED: pictures for each season, LIFEPAC Tablet, pencils, crayons, Worksheet 15

TEACHING PAGES 36 and 37:

Discuss the seasons as they are in your area.

Review the names of the seasons. Note that autumn is often called fall.

Match the names of the seasons with pictures .

Read the short poem on page 36.

Have the children find the vocabulary words.

Have a child read the question at the bottom of the page.

Read the direction: Write the seasons in order. Do it orally with the group first. Repeat several times. Begin with a different season each time.

Illustrate if necessary by writing the names in a circle. Title it "Around the Year."

Have the children complete page 36 independently.

Read the direction on page 37.

Have the children complete the page independently.

Check together and discuss their pictures .

SEASONS

Summer is hot.
Winter is not.
Autumn and spring
Are in between.

What is the season now?

Write the seasons in order. Use your Tablet. Start with winter.

winter

spring

summer

autumn

page 36 (thirty-six)

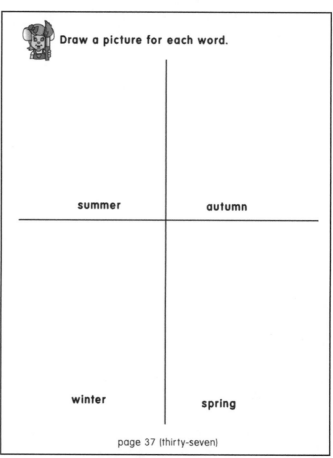

Draw a picture for each word.

summer | autumn

winter | spring

page 37 (thirty-seven)

ACTIVITY:

Do Worksheet 15.

All the necessary instructions are found on the Worksheet. Read them to the children.

Name _____

Make a summer tree or a fall tree.

Take colored paper (green for summer, or orange, yellow, red for fall).
Cut out small leaves.
Paste them to the tree.
Color the other parts of the picture.
Color the sky.

Write summer or fall. _summer (fall)_

Science: 107
Worksheet 15
with page 37

Teacher check _____
Initial   Date

Page 38: Activity Page

MATERIALS NEEDED: crayons, pencils

TEACHING PAGE 38:

Read the direction. Review the four words for the seasons. Ask the children what other name is given to fall (autumn).

Have the children do the page independently.

Check together by having the children tell how they knew what season was shown in each picture.

ACTIVITY:

Make a seasons booklet or bulletin board.

Have the children find or draw pictures of different signs and activities for each season.

page 38 (thirty-eight)

Page 39: Activity Page

MATERIALS NEEDED: pencils, crayons, LIFEPAC Tablets

TEACHING PAGE 39:

Read the direction. Tell the children to refer back to page 38 for the spelling of the season.

When the picture is finished, have the children write a two or three paragraph story about their favorite season. Remind them to tell why it is their favorite season, to write in complete sentences, to spell words correctly and to ask for help with words they cannot spell, to write neatly, and to check their work.

Allow class time for the next few days for children to read their stories and show their pictures.

Use the discussion time to reinforce and to review concepts taught in the LIFEPAC.

Draw your favorite season.

My favorite season is _____

Teacher Check _____
　　　　　　　　　Initial　　　Date

page 39 (thirty-nine)

Pages 40 and 41: Self Test 3

CONCEPT: evaluation

OBJECTIVES: I can tell about different kinds of land.
I can tell about different bodies of water.
I can tell about different weather.

READING INTEGRATION: following written directions, recalling details

VOCABULARY: Review all the vocabulary words.

MATERIALS NEEDED: pencils, Worksheet 16, scissors, crayons, envelopes

TEACHING PAGES 40 and 41:

Review the vocabulary and concepts for the entire LIFEPAC, with special emphasis on section 3.

Read through the directions for self test with the group. Answer any questions they might have.

The general proficiency of your group will dictate whether you choose to direct the self test or allow the children to proceed independently, once directions are given.

In either case, you should be available to answer questions and to help with vocabulary, as needed.

For those children who need extra help, have them work with a classroom helper or a parent to prepare for the LIFEPAC Test. Take home activity: Distribute Worksheet 16- "A Beautiful Day."

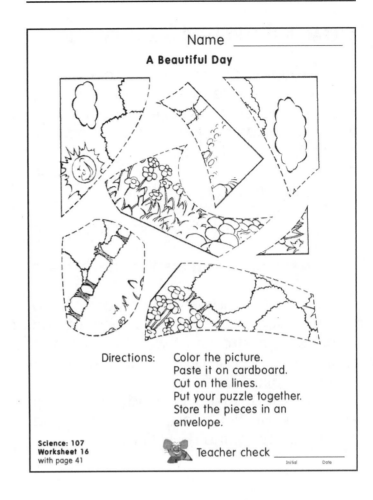

Name _____

A Beautiful Day

Directions: Color the picture.
Paste it on cardboard.
Cut on the lines.
Put your puzzle together.
Store the pieces in an
envelope.

Science: 107
Worksheet 16
with page 41

Teacher check _____
Initial   Date

LIFEPAC TEST AND ALTERNATE LIFEPAC TEST:

Administer the test to the class as a group. Ask to have directions read or read them to the class. In either case, be sure that the children clearly understand. Put examples on the board if it seems necessary. Give ample time for for each activity to be completed before going on to the next.

Correct immediately and discuss with the child.

Review any concepts that have been missed.

Give those children who do not achieve the 80% score additional copies of the worksheets and a list of vocabulary words to study. A parent or a classroom helper should help in the review.

When the child is ready, give the Alternate LIFEPAC Test. Use the same procedure as for the LIFEPAC Test.

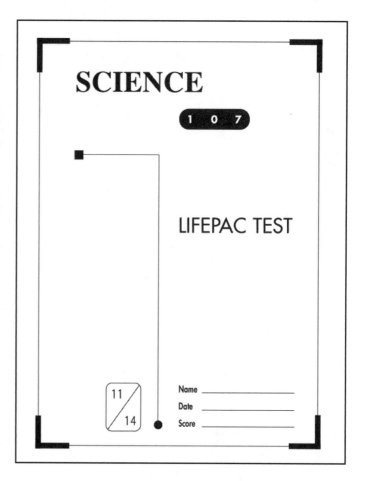

SCIENCE

1 0 7

LIFEPAC TEST

11/14

Name _____
Date _____
Score _____

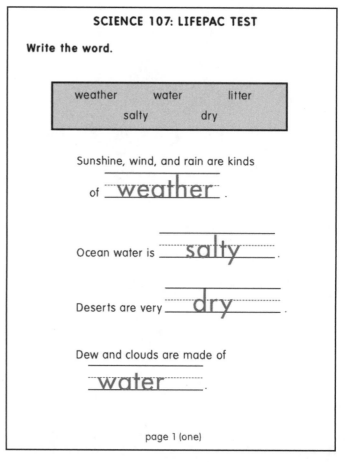

SCIENCE 107: LIFEPAC TEST

Write the word.

weather	water	litter
salty	dry	

Sunshine, wind, and rain are kinds

of _weather_ .

Ocean water is _salty_ .

Deserts are very _dry_ .

Dew and clouds are made of

water .

page 1 (one)

112

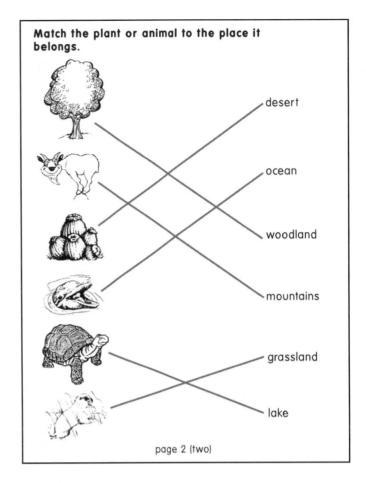

Match the plant or animal to the place it belongs.

desert

ocean

woodland

mountains

grassland

lake

page 2 (two)

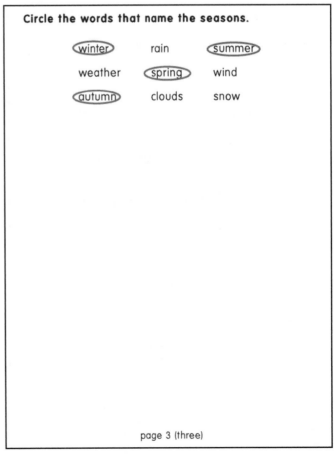

Circle the words that name the seasons.

winter   rain   summer

weather   spring   wind

autumn   clouds   snow

page 3 (three)

SCIENCE

1 0 7

ALTERNATE LIFEPAC TEST

10/13

Name _____

Date _____

Score _____

SCIENCE 107: ALTERNATE LIFEPAC TEST

Write the answer.

Snow and sunshine are kinds of __weather__.
weather   seasons

Each year has __four__ seasons.
two   four

You find water in __oceans__.
oceans   deserts

Deserts are very __dry__.
dry   wet

page 1 (one)

Name the seasons.

| spring | autumn | summer | winter |

__winter__   __autumn__

__summer__   __spring__

page 2 (two)

Match the animal to its home.

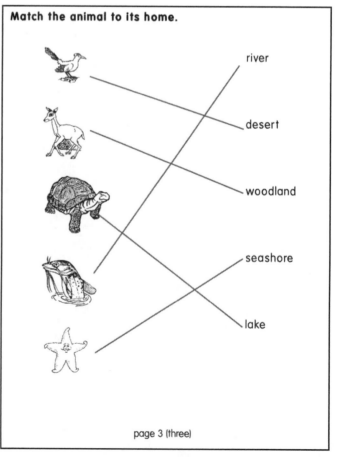

river

desert

woodland

seashore

lake

page 3 (three)

Page 1: All About Energy

CONCEPTS: Introduction to concepts of LIFEPAC 108: sources, uses, and conservation of energy.

OBJECTIVE: Introduction to the objectives of LIFEPAC 108

READING INTEGRATION: main idea

VOCABULARY: energy, (Sunny)

MATERIALS NEEDED: vocabulary word cards; picture of Sunny

TEACHING PAGE 1:

Show the picture of Sunny, a friend who will help the children learn about energy.

Present the vocabulary word, *energy*. Have the children show ways they use energy. Ask how they would act if they had no energy.

Simple definition: Energy is power that makes things go (work, move).

Have the children write their own names on the line provided.

Read the introduction to the class.

Have the children find the vocabulary words.

Ask to have the pictures identified. (sunny and the sun)

Read the objectives. Be sure the children understand that these are things they will be able to do when they have finished LIFEPAC 108.

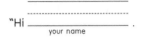

ALL ABOUT ENERGY

"Hi _____ .
your name

My name is Sunny.
I am using energy.
Using energy is fun.

Come with me.
We will find out
about energy.
We will learn where it comes from.
We will find out how to save it, too."

 Objectives

1. I can tell about energy God gives us.
2. I can tell how energy is used.
3 I can tell some ways to save energy.

page 1 (one)

I. PART ONE

Page 2: God Gives Energy

CONCEPTS: The three important concepts of section I are introduced here: God made the world; everything that grows or changes needs energy; the sun provides energy.

OBJECTIVE: I can tell about energy God gives us.

BIBLE REFERENCES: Genesis 1:1; 1:16 and 1 7

PROCESS: observing

READING INTEGRATION: main ideas, recalling detail

VOCABULARY: (grow, change)

MATERIALS NEEDED: vocabulary word cards; pictures of things that grow and change: plants, animals, people; LIFEPAC Tablets; pencils

TEACHING PAGE 2:
Present the vocabulary words if they are not familiar to the group.

Read the page to the students, or have it read by a volunteer.

Use the story of the Creation (Genesis 1) to verify that God made the world and the sun.

Ask: "What does the sun give to the world?" (energy, light, heat) *Note:* Both heat and light are kinds of energy.

ACTIVITY:
Have the children write these sentences in their Tablets.

"God made the world."
"God made the sun."
"Thank you, God."

I. GOD GIVES ENERGY

God made the world.
Everything in God's world
that grows needs energy.
Everything in God's world
that changes needs energy.
God made the sun.
The sun gives energy to the world.

page 2 (two)

Page 3: Activity Page

MATERIALS NEEDED: pencils, crayons, alphabet charts

TEACHING PAGE 3:

Read the directions to the class or have them read by a volunteer.

The children may complete the page independently.

ACTIVITY:

Set up a book table including books about the sun, wind, and water. They may be used for independent reading and for activities.

Follow the dots to find where energy comes from. Start with <u>a</u>.

Color the picture. Draw yourself in the picture.

page 3 (three)

Page 4: Sun

CONCEPT: Light energy and heat energy come from the sun.

OBJECTIVE: I can tell about energy God gives us.

PROCESS: observing

READING INTEGRATION: vocabulary development, recalling detail

VOCABULARY: (light, heat)

MATERIALS NEEDED: vocabulary word cards, lamp (no shade), LIFEPAC Tablet, pencils, Worksheet 1

TEACHING PAGE 4:
Present the vocabulary. Have the children volunteer names of things that give light. Ask what sense is used to observe light. (eye/sight)

Have the children volunteer names of things that give heat. Ask what sense is used to observe heat (skin/touch/feel).

Use an unshaded lamp to simulate the sun. Have the children note (without actually touching the bulb) that when light is produced, heat is also produced.

Read the page to the children or have it read by a volunteer.

Ask: "How does Sunny feel in the picture?" (Her feet are hot.)

"What made the sidewalk hot?" (the heat from the sun)

ACTIVITIES:
1. Have the children write in their Tablets:
    "The sun gives light."
    "The sun gives heat."
2. Provide Worksheet 1.

Read the directions. Discuss the picture and the two sentences before the children begin to color.

Sun

God made the sun.
The sun gives light.
Light is energy.
We can <u>see</u> light.

Light energy changes.
It changes
to heat energy.
We can <u>feel</u> heat.

IT'S SO HOT WHEN THE SUN IS OUT!

OH, THIS IS HOT!

page 4 (four)

Name _____

Color the picture.

Read the sentence.
Sunny can <u>see</u> the light.
Sunny can <u>feel</u> the heat.

Science: 108
Worksheet 1
with page 4

Teacher check _____
Initial   Date

Page 5: Activity Page

MATERIALS NEEDED: pencil

TEACHING PAGE 5:

Ask a volunteer to read the direction.

Go over the words in the box and the sentences, if necessary.

Have the children complete the page independently giving individual help, as needed.

Check it together as reinforcement.

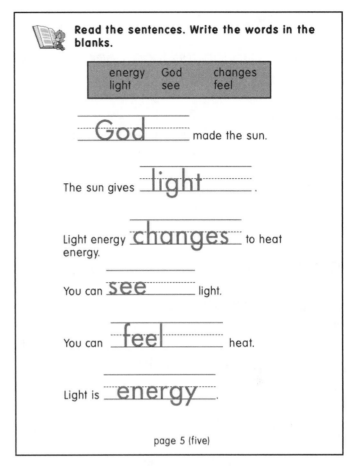

Read the sentences. Write the words in the blanks.

energy	God	changes
light	see	feel

God _____ made the sun.

The sun gives light _____.

Light energy changes to heat energy.

You can see _____ light.

You can feel _____ heat.

Light is energy.

page 5 (five)

119

Page 6: Energy

CONCEPT: Through the food chain, people get energy from the sun.

OBJECTIVE:
  I can tell about energy God gives us.
  I can tell about energy we use.

PROCESSES: observing, classifying (plants animals eat, plants people eat, animals people eat)

READING INTEGRATION: main idea

MATERIALS NEEDED: LIFEPAC Tablet, pencil, crayons, pictures of plants that animals eat, plants that people eat, and animals that people eat (see Science 106)

TEACHING PAGE 6:
  Read the text to the class with the students following along. As you complete each section spend some time discussing the plants or animals and the part they play in the food/energy chain from sun to man.

ACTIVITIES:
  1.   Provide Worksheet 2.
  Read the directions. Discuss the ways portrayed that we get energy. Remind the children to trace the path first with their fingers before using a pencil.
  Check together and ask the children to give further examples of plants and animals they eat.
  2.   Have the children write this sentence in their Tablets.
  Energy comes from the sun.

Plants need light energy and heat energy to grow.
Plants use this energy to make food.

Some animals eat the plants.
Animals use this food to give them energy to move and grow.

Plants and animals are food for us.
The food made from the sun's energy helps us move and grow.

page 6 (six)

Name _____

Find two ways energy gets to you.

Science: 108
Worksheet 2
with page 6

Teacher check _____
Initial   Date

Page 7: Activity Page

MATERIALS NEEDED: pencil, crayons, LIFEPAC Tablet

TEACHING PAGE 7:

Ask a student to read the direction.

Have the children complete their pictures independently.

As you share the completed pictures emphasize the fact that energy's hidden use for work and play comes from the food they eat and through the food/energy chain from the sun.

ACTIVITY:

Have the children write two paragraphs about plants they like to eat. Help with the spelling. Allow time for the children to read their paragraphs and discuss them in groups.

Draw five plants that you like to eat.

page 7 (seven)

Pages 8 and 9: Wind

CONCEPTS: Moving air (wind) has energy. Wind energy can do work.

OBJECTIVE: I can tell about energy God gives us.

PROCESSES: observing, comparing

READING INTEGRATION: main idea, vocabulary development, recalling details, following directions

VOCABULARY: air, still, moving, wind, windmill, wheel, electricity

MATERIALS NEEDED: vocabulary word cards, LIFEPAC Tablet, pencil, electric fan with paper streamers attached to simulate wind, pen, stick or straw, Worksheet 3, pinwheel, picture of windmill

TEACHING PAGES 8 and 9:

Present the vocabulary words.

Demonstrate differences between still air and wind by using the fan. Note that you cannot see the wind, but you can see what it does to other things.

Read the page to the class, or have it read by a volunteer.

Discuss the picture.

Ask: "Which picture shows wind?" "How can you tell?"

Do Worksheet 3 before beginning page 9.

Have the children use their pinwheels to learn how it takes very little air to turn the little wheel. Experiment with the fan, blowing by mouth, and just turning around pulling the pinwheel through the air.

Discuss windmills and the work they do. Do the same with the word *electricity*.

Read the text at the top of page 9 to the class, or have it read by a volunteer. This paragraph will review your preparation activities.

Ask a child to identify and read the direction sentences.

WIND

God made the air.
Sometimes the air is still.
You cannot <u>hear</u> the air.
You cannot <u>feel</u> the air.
You cannot <u>see</u> the air.
Suddenly the air changes.
It moves.
You can <u>hear</u> the moving air.
You can <u>feel</u> the moving air.
You cannot <u>see</u> the moving air.
You <u>can</u> <u>see</u> what
the moving air is doing.
Moving air is wind.
Wind is energy.

page 8 (eight)

📖 **Read this story.**

The Big Wind Did It

One day Chuck and Buck were riding in a truck.

A big wind
picked up the truck
and put it in a muddy hole.
"Oh, oh!" said Chuck.
"We are stuck."
"Yes," said Buck.
"We have a stuck truck."
Chuck and Buck were sad.

Mr. Crest saw them.
He had his best horses,
Hank and Frank.
Hank and Frank tried
to yank the stuck truck
out of the mud.
The truck was still stuck.

"I know," said Mr. Crest.
"I will get Farmer Zest.
He has a tractor."

page 10 (ten)

Have the children complete the activity independently. Check it together.

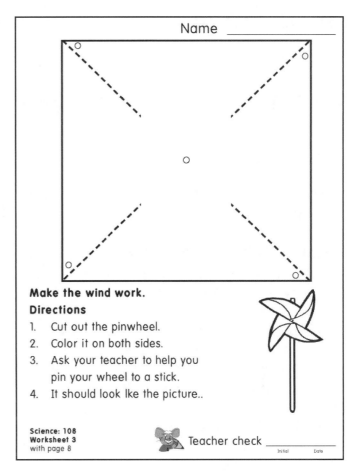

Name _____

Make the wind work.

Directions

1. Cut out the pinwheel.
2. Color it on both sides.
3. Ask your teacher to help you pin your wheel to a stick.
4. It should look lke the picture..

Science: 108
Worksheet 3
with page 8

Teacher check _____
Initial   Date

Pages 10 and 11: Story

CONCEPT: Wind has energy to move things.

OBJECTIVE: I can tell about energy God gives us.

PROCESS: observing

READING INTEGRATION: fact or fantasy, rhyming words, sequencing

VOCABULARY: Present the words that rhyme, if you wish, to help the children follow the story (optional).

MATERIALS NEEDED: rhyming word cards and pictures representing the words (optional), Worksheets 4 and 5, scissors, paste, crayons

TEACHING PAGES 10 and 11:

"The Big Wind Did It" is a fanciful story about a very strong wind.

It is designed to help the children differentiate between fact and fantasy.

This story is primarily a read-aloud story. It is, however, easily adaptable as a flannel board story. Have fun with it.

When the story is finished have the children try to retell it in their own words.

Discuss what really strong winds can do (tornado, hurricane, and so on).

ACTIVITY:

Provide Worksheets 4 and 5.

Read the directions on Worksheet 4. Have the children repeat the directions.

Let them do the pages independently.

Check by having the children retell the story in their own words from the pictures.

Read this story.

The Big Wind Did It

One day Chuck and Buck were riding in a truck.

A big wind picked up the truck and put it in a muddy hole. "Oh, oh!" said Chuck. "We are stuck." "Yes," said Buck. "We have a stuck truck." Chuck and Buck were sad.

Mr. Crest saw them. He had his best horses, Hank and Frank. Hank and Frank tried to yank the stuck truck out of the mud. The truck was still stuck.

"I know," said Mr. Crest. "I will get Farmer Zest. He has a tractor."

page 10 (ten)

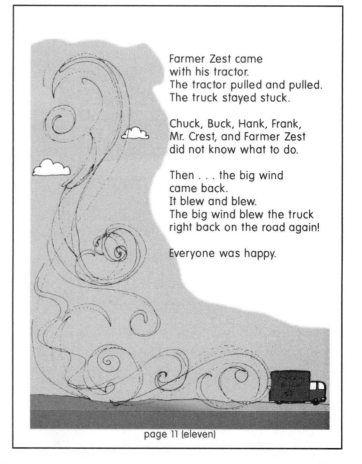

Farmer Zest came with his tractor. The tractor pulled and pulled. The truck stayed stuck.

Chuck, Buck, Hank, Frank, Mr. Crest, and Farmer Zest did not know what to do.

Then . . . the big wind came back. It blew and blew. The big wind blew the truck right back on the road again!

Everyone was happy.

page 11 (eleven)

Name _____

Color the pictures.
Cut them apart.
Put them in order.
Glue them onto Worksheet 5.

Science: 108
Worksheet 4
with page 11

Teacher check _____
　　　　　　　　　Initial　　　Date

Name _____

The Big Wind Did it

1.	2.
3.	4.

Science: 108
Worksheet 5
with page 11

Teacher check _____
　　　　　　　　　Initial　　　Date

Page 12: Activity Page

VOCABULARY: true, fact, fantasy, make-believe

MATERIALS NEEDED: pencils

TEACHING PAGE 12:

Read and discuss the fact/fantasy section at the top of the page. Have the children name some stories they know that are fact (true).

Have them name some stories they know are fantasy (make-believe).

Ask for a volunteer to find and read the direction sentence.

Have them complete the activity independently. Check it together.

Some stories are **true**.
They are **fact**.

Some stories are **make-believe**.
They are **fantasy**.

Write the word that goes with the story.

"The Big Wind Did It" is a

fantasy .
fact / fantasy

A big wind ____can____ move a truck.
can / cannot

A tractor cannot move a truck.
can / cannot

page 12 (twelve)

Page 13 : Activity Page

MATERIALS NEEDED: crayons

TEACHING PAGE 13:

Ask a volunteer to identify and read the direction sentence.

Have the children complete their pictures independently.

Give each child an opportunity to tell about his picture.

page 13 (thirteen)

Pages 14 and 15: Water

CONCEPTS:
God made water.
People, animals, and plants need water.
Moving water has energy.
Steam has energy.

OBJECTIVES:
I can tell about energy God gives us.
I can tell about energy we use

BIBLE REFERENCE: Genesis 1:1 through 10

PROCESSES: observing, comparing predicting

READING INTEGRATION: recalling detail, main idea, vocabulary development, speaking in a group, sequencing

VOCABULARY: steam, engines, trains raindrop

MATERIALS NEEDED: word cards, pictures of water at work (water wheels and so on), Worksheet 6, pencils, crayons

TEACHING PAGES 14 and 15:
Use the verses of Genesis to show how God created and divided the waters.

Discuss the importance of water to life as it has been taught in earlier LIFEPACs.

Tell that now they will learn how the energy of water can be used to do work.

Read the text to the children, allowing time for discussion of each concept as it is mentioned.

Example: Ask the children where they might see water moving fast. What can water move?

Read the sentences at the top of page 15 to the class.

Have the children read the picture story to themselves, then tell about the places the raindrop has been in the right order.

Discussion: "Where will the raindrop land next time he comes?"

WATER

God made water.
We need water to drink.
Plants need water to help
them grow.

Sometimes water is still.
Still water has no energy
to do work.

Sometimes water moves
very fast.
Water moves things.
Moving water has energy.

Sometimes water gets hot.
It changes to steam.
Steam has energy.
Steam can drive engines.
Steam engines can pull
trains.

page 14 (fourteen)

The sun helps water do its work.
Every drop of water is used
over and over again.

Where will the raindrop land
the next time it comes?

Experiment **Make water work.**

You need:	
pan	sand
board	small stones
glass of water	large stone

page 15 (fifteen)

Give the children an opportunity to share their ideas.

ACTIVITY:

Do Worksheet 6.

Read the directions. Allow time for discussion of the drawings when the children have finished.

Note: The materials listed on the bottom of page 15 go with the demonstration activity on page 16.

Name _____

Draw the raindrop.
Draw a place it might land the next time it comes.

Science: 108
Worksheet 6
with page 15

Teacher check _____
Initial   Date

Page 16: Activity Page

VOCABULARY: board stone(s), sand, stayed, (pour, still)

MATERIALS NEEDED: pan, board, stones (large and small), sand, glass of water

TEACHING PAGE 16:

Collect the materials listed above (and on page 15). Set them up for a demonstration or in a discovery center where each child will have an opportunity to do the experiment.

Demonstrate the experiment step by step as on the page or read through the directions for the children to prepare them for the activity in the discovery center.

When the demonstration or center activity has been finished, the children should complete the page. Give individual help as needed.

Discussion: Ask the children to predict what might happen to the stones and sand if a hose were used instead of a glass of water.

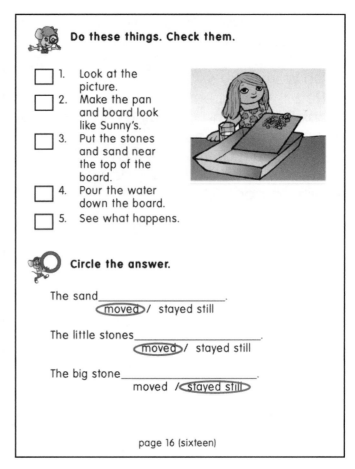

Do these things. Check them.

☐ 1. Look at the picture.
☐ 2. Make the pan and board look like Sunny's.
☐ 3. Put the stones and sand near the top of the board.
☐ 4. Pour the water down the board.
☐ 5. See what happens.

Circle the answer.

The sand_____.
  (moved)/ stayed still

The little stones_____.
  (moved)/ stayed still

The big stone_____.
  moved /(stayed still)

page 16 (sixteen)

Pages 17 and 18: Self Test 1

CONCEPT: evaluation

OBJECTIVES:
I can tell about energy God gave us.
I can tell about energy we use.

READING INTEGRATION: following written directions, recalling details

VOCABULARY: Review all the vocabulary.

MATERIALS NEEDED: pencils, Worksheet 7

TEACHING PAGES 17 and 18:
Review the vocabulary and concepts of section 1.
Read all the directions with the children. Be sure they are understood.
The general proficiency of your group should dictate whether you choose to direct the self test or allow the children to proceed independently, once directions are given.
In either case you should be available to answer questions and to help with the vocabulary as needed.

ACTIVITY:
Provide Worksheet 7.
Read the direction. Let the children do this sheet independently for review or enrichment. Check individually with those children who did poorly on the test. Ask the child to explain each picture and to tell what he remembers about it from this LIFEPAC.

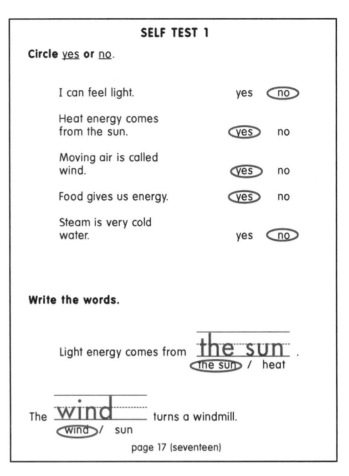

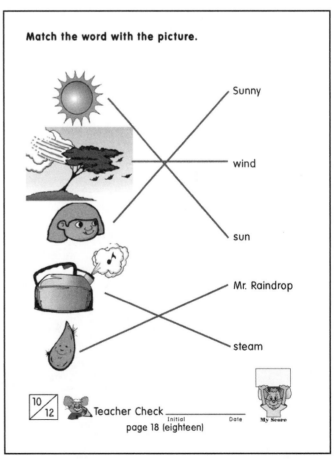

Name _____

Draw a picture for each energy word.

sun	plants
wind	animals
water	you

Science: 108
Worksheet 7
with page 18

Teacher check _____

Initial   Date

II. PART TWO

Page 19: We Use Energy

CONCEPTS:
We use the energy God gives us.
Introduce the kinds of energy we use.

OBJECTIVE: I can tell about energy we use.

PROCESSES: observing, comparing

READING INTEGRATION: main idea, recalling detail

VOCABULARY: fuel, solar, nuclear

MATERIALS NEEDED: vocabulary word cards, pictures representing the vocabulary

TEACHING PAGE 19:

Review the sources of energy from section 1: sun, wind, and water. Ask where these energy sources come from (given by God).

Present the vocabulary. The words will become more familiar as you work through the section. The children should see them now as kinds of energy. They will learn more about the words as they do section 2.

Read the text to the class or have it read by volunteers. Discuss each section of the page briefly as you read. Cite examples of each kind of energy.

ACTIVITY:

Prepare a book table including books about electricity, fuels, and solar and nuclear energy, as available.

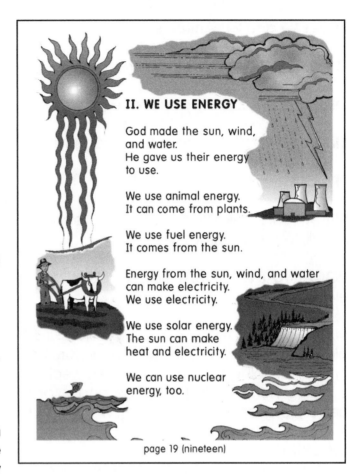

II. WE USE ENERGY

God made the sun, wind, and water.
He gave us their energy to use.

We use animal energy. It can come from plants.

We use fuel energy. It comes from the sun.

Energy from the sun, wind, and water can make electricity. We use electricity.

We use solar energy. The sun can make heat and electricity.

We can use nuclear energy, too.

page 19 (nineteen)

Pages 20 and 21: Animals

CONCEPT: We use animals for energy.

OBJECTIVE: I can tell about energy we use.

BIBLE REFERENCE: Genesis 8: 6 through 12

PROCESS: observing

READING INTEGRATION: main idea, recalling detail, following directions

VOCABULARY: dove, Noah, donkey, Mary, elephant

MATERIALS NEEDED: vocabulary word cards, pictures representing the words, pictures of animals helping people (examples: seeing-eye dog, horse pulling a wagon, and so on), pencils, crayons, LIFEPAC Tablet, Worksheet 8

TEACHING PAGES 20 and 21:

Present the vocabulary. Read the text to the children or have it read by volunteers. Discuss the sentences as they are read.

Refer to Genesis 8:6 through 12 for the story of how the dove helped Noah.
Ask the children to share ideas of how the donkey might have helped Mary. Refer to the picture at the top of the page.

Ask a child to find and read the two direction sentences on page 21.

When the children understand what to do, have them complete both activities independently.

Give individual help, as needed. Check the page together. Provide opportunity for children to show and tell about their pictures.

ACTIVITIES:

1. Have the children write this sentence in their Tablets.
   Animals help us do work.
2. Children who are able may write a sentence or two about their pictures describing how the animal is helping.

WE USE ANIMALS

People and animals get energy from the food they eat.

Animals help people do work. Animals in the Bible helped.

A horse helps a farmer.

A dove helped Noah.

A donkey may have helped Mary.

page 20 (twenty)

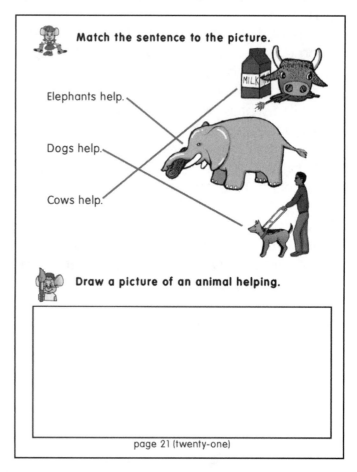

Match the sentence to the picture.

Elephants help.

Dogs help.

Cows help.

Draw a picture of an animal helping.

page 21 (twenty-one)

3. Do Worksheet 8.

Read the sentence and direction to the children.

Let them complete the page. Discuss how elephants help.

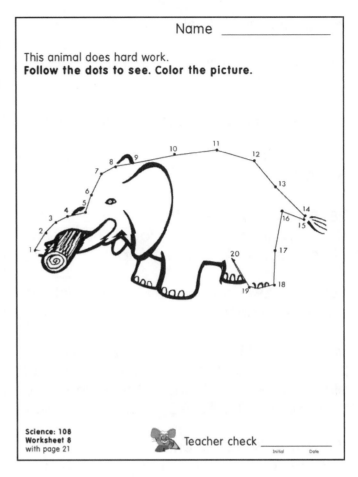

Name _____

This animal does hard work.
Follow the dots to see. Color the picture.

Science: 108
Worksheet 8
with page 21

Teacher check _____
Initial   Date

135

Pages 22 and 23: Fuels

CONCEPT: We use energy produced by burning fuels.

OBJECTIVE: I can tell about energy we use.

PROCESSES: observing, comparing, predicting

READING INTEGRATION: vocabulary development, main idea, following directions, speaking in a group

VOCABULARY: fuel, burn, wood, coal, oil, gasoline, (ground)

MATERIALS NEEDED: vocabulary word cards; pictures or samples of fuels, pictures of places they are found, places they are burned; pencils; LIFEPAC Tablet; Worksheet 9

TEACHING PAGES 22 and 23:

Present the vocabulary. Match the vocabulary with the corresponding pictures or objects.

Read the text aloud, section by section, identifying the vocabulary and matching it with the pictures as you go.

Discuss each fuel, its source, and how it is used.

Ask for a volunteer to find and read the direction.

Have the children complete the activity independently. Check it together and discuss.

Note: Some of the energy the cow gets from eating grass is passed along to us as we consume dairy products and beef.

ACTIVITIES:

1. *ENRICHMENT:* Ask the children to guess which fuels might have been used in Bible times.

Note: Oil burned in those days was olive oil, not the petroleum products we use today. It was burned for light. Wood was burned for cooking.

WE USE FUELS

A fuel is something we burn to get energy.

Wood is a fuel.
Wood is from a tree.

Coal is a fuel.
Coal comes from under the ground.

Oil is a fuel.
Oil is under the ground, too.

Gasoline is a fuel.
Gasoline is made from oil.

Food is a fuel, too.
Animals need food.
We need food.
Food gives energy.

page 22 (twenty-two)

Match the picture with the fuel.

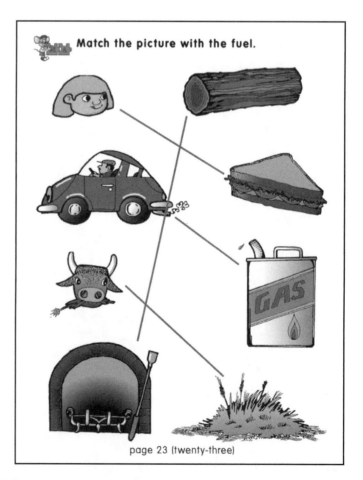

page 23 (twenty-three)

2.   Do Worksheet 9.

Read the direction.

Make sure the children know what each picture is before they begin.

Check together and talk about each fuel, where it is found, and how it is obtained.

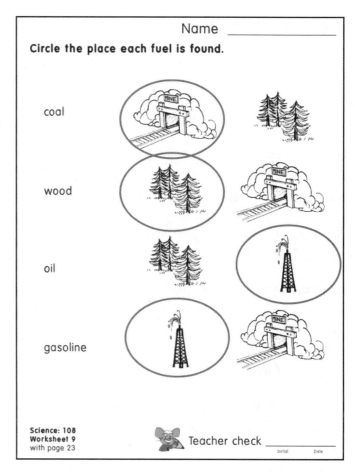

Name _____

Circle the place each fuel is found.

coal

wood

oil

gasoline

Science: 108
Worksheet 9
with page 23

Teacher check _____

Initial   Date

137

Page 24: Electricity

CONCEPT: Electricity is produced by other kinds of energy.

OBJECTIVE: I can tell about energy we use.

PROCESSES: observing, comparing

READING INTEGRATION: main idea

VOCABULARY: important, (steam, water, wind, fuel)

MATERIALS NEEDED: vocabulary word cards, pictures of water power producing electricity (dam), wind power producing electricity (windmill), and fuel burning electric plant

TEACHING PAGE 24:
Present the vocabulary. Review the words wind, water, steam, and fuel.

Read the text aloud or have it read by volunteers. Share the pictures and discuss each source of electricity.

Provide an opportunity for the children to discuss ways they use electricity everyday.

ACTIVITIES:
1.   Read or tell the story of how Benjamin Franklin discovered electricity by flying his kite in a lightning storm.
2.   Do Worksheet 10.

Discuss the picture with the children after you have told or read them the Benjamin Franklin story.

Let them color the picture.

Tell them to write a paragraph about Benjamin Franklin and electricity in their Tablets. Allow time to share the paragraphs.

WE USE ELECTRICITY

Electricity is important.
Men make electricity
from other kinds of energy.

Moving water
can make electricity.

Wind can make electricity.

Burning fuel changes water
into steam.
Steam can make electricity.

page 24 (twenty-four)

Name _____

Color Benjamin Franklin and his kite.

Science: 108
Worksheet 10
with page 24

Teacher check _____
Initial   Date

Page 25: Activity Page

MATERIALS NEEDED: pencils, crayons

TEACHING PAGE 25:

Have a student find and read the two direction sentences.

Have the children complete the activities independently.

Check it together.

The children may wish to color the picture.

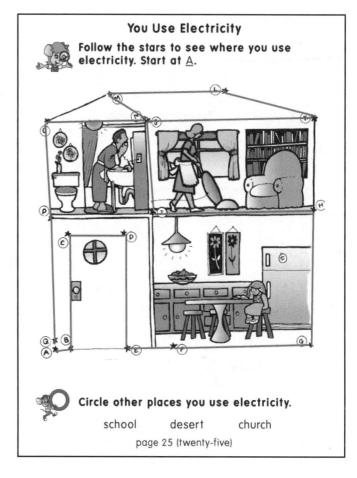

Page 26: New Ways to Make Energy

CONCEPT: We are learning new ways to use energy from the sun (solar energy).

OBJECTIVE: I can tell about energy we use.

PROCESSES: observing, comparing

READING INTEGRATION: vocabulary development, main idea

VOCABULARY: solar

MATERIALS NEEDED: word card, pictures of the sun, pictures of solar collectors, magnifying glass

TEACHING PAGE 26:

Present the vocabulary word, *solar,* with the picture of the sun. Emphasize that solar means of the sun. Tell the children that we are learning new ways to use the greatest source of energy God has given us, the sun's energy.

Read the text aloud or have it read by volunteers. Show the pictures of solar collectors. Ask the children to share any experience they might have had with solar energy.

ACTIVITY:

Demonstrate how collecting direct rays from the sun through a magnifying glass can burn a hole in a piece of paper.

Note: The glass concentrates the sun's rays to produce enough heat to burn the paper. Solar collectors concentrate the rays to heat water or cook food.

WE LEARN OTHER WAYS TO MAKE ENERGY

The sun has lots of energy.
It is called solar energy.
We are learning to use
solar energy in new ways.
We can cook food
with solar energy.

We can heat water
for our homes
with solar energy.

Solar energy
can make electricity, too.

page 26 (twenty-six)

Page 27: Activity Pages

MATERIALS NEEDED: pencils, LIFEPAC Tablet

TEACHING PAGE 27:

Ask for volunteers to find and read the three direction sentences.

Have the children complete the page independently, giving individual help as needed.

Check the page together. Discuss each answer to review the concepts.

Have the children read their sentences aloud.

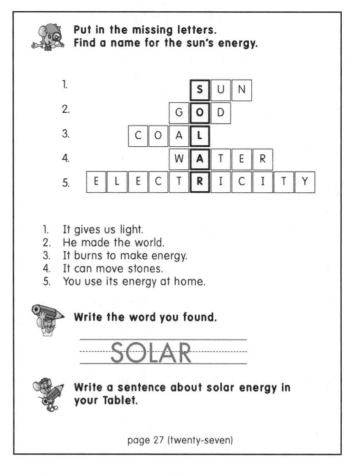

Put in the missing letters.
Find a name for the sun's energy.

1. | S | U | N |
2. G O D
3. C O A L
4. W A T E R
5. E L E C T R I C I T Y

1. It gives us light.
2. He made the world.
3. It burns to make energy.
4. It can move stones.
5. You use its energy at home.

Write the word you found.

SOLAR

Write a sentence about solar energy in your Tablet.

page 27 (twenty-seven)

Pages 28, 29, and 30: Nuclear Energy

CONCEPTS:
Introduce the idea of nuclear energy and the vocabulary involved to present it. Scientists discovered nuclear energy.

OBJECTIVE: I can tell about energy we use.

PROCESSES: observing, comparing

READING INTEGRATION: vocabulary development, reading a rebus story, fact/fantasy, main idea

VOCABULARY: atom, dot, electricity, eye, magnifying glass, microscope, pencil, scientist

MATERIALS NEEDED: word cards, pictures as on the page

TEACHING PAGES 28, 29, and 30:

Present the vocabulary words with the corresponding pictures. Play a matching game with the pictures and words.

Explain that these words will help them read a true story about another kind of energy.

Ask a child to read the direction sentences.

Have the children take turns reading the picture words.

Give the children an opportunity to read the story to themselves.

Ask volunteers to take turns reading it aloud while the others follow along (round robin).

Then have all read aloud together.

Ask these questions: "Can you see an atom with your eyes?" (no) "Can you see an atom with a magnifying glass?" (no)

"What did the scientists use to see an atom?" (microscope)

"What did the scientist do to an atom that made heat energy?" (split it) "What do we call energy made by splitting atoms?" (nuclear energy)

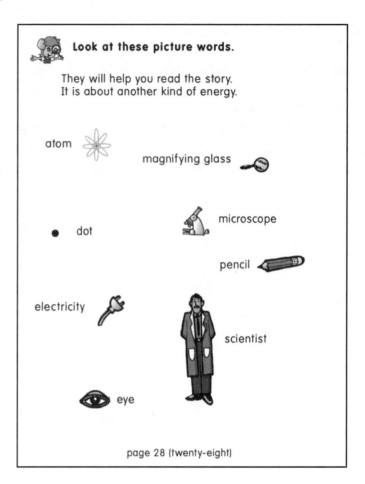

page 28 (twenty-eight)

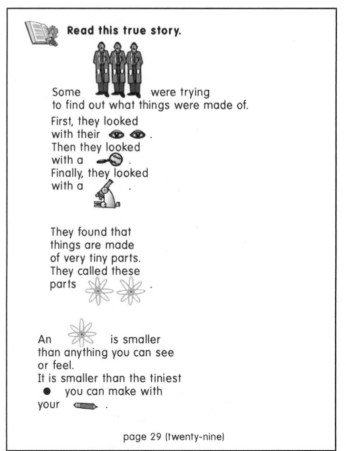

page 29 (twenty-nine)

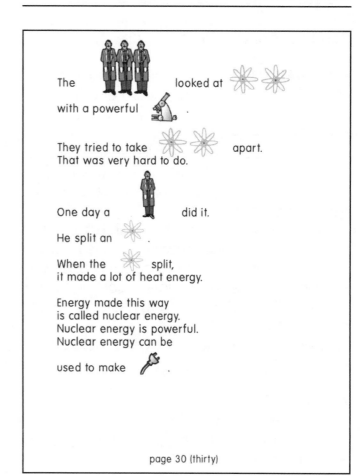

The looked at with a powerful .

They tried to take apart.
That was very hard to do.

One day a did it.

He split an .

When the split,
it made a lot of heat energy.

Energy made this way
is called nuclear energy.
Nuclear energy is powerful.
Nuclear energy can be

used to make .

page 30 (thirty)

143

Page 31: Activity Page

MATERIALS NEEDED: pencils, Worksheets 11 and 12, crayons, scissors, paste or glue

TEACHING PAGE 31:

Have the children recall the story about the Big Wind and the Stuck Truck. *Ask:* "Was that story fact (true) or fantasy (make-believe)?" (fantasy)

Ask about the story they just read. Was it fact (true) or fantasy (make-believe)? (fact)

Ask a child to find and read the direction sentence. Have the children complete the page independently, giving individual help as needed.

Check it together, reviewing the story as you check.

ACTIVITY:

Do Worksheets 11 and 12.

Read the directions. Have the children repeat them.

When they have completed the sheets, check by having the children retell the story.

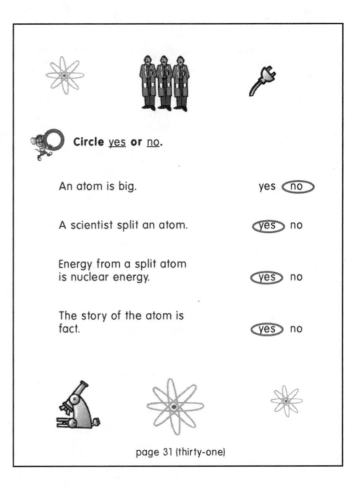

Circle <u>yes</u> or <u>no</u>.

An atom is big.	yes (no)
A scientist split an atom.	(yes) no
Energy from a split atom is nuclear energy.	(yes) no
The story of the atom is fact.	(yes) no

page 31 (thirty-one)

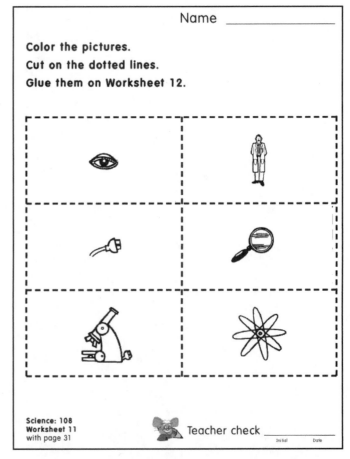

Name _____

Color the pictures.
Cut on the dotted lines.
Glue them on Worksheet 12.

Science: 108
Worksheet 11
with page 31

Teacher check _____
Initial   Date

Name _____

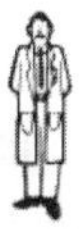

Scientists looked for answers.	They looked with their **eyes**.
They looked with a **magnifying glass.**	They looked with a **microscope.**
Scientists learned about **atoms.**	Nuclear energy can make **electricity.**

Science: 108
Worksheet 12
with page 31

Teacher check _____
Initial   Date

Pages 32 and 33: Self Test 2

CONCEPT: evaluation

OBJECTIVES:
I can tell about energy God gives us.
I can tell about energy we use.

READING INTEGRATION: following directions, recalling details

VOCABULARY: Review al! the vocabulary.

MATERIALS NEEDED: pencils, Worksheet 13, crayons

TEACHING PAGES 32 and 33:
Review the vocabulary and concepts for sections 1 and 2.
Read all the directions with your group. Be sure they are understood.
The general proficiency of your group will dictate whether you choose to direct the self test or allow the children to proceed independently, once the directions are given.
In either case you should be available to answer questions and to help with vocabulary, as needed.
Have the children who need the review go over the first two sections with their parents or a classroom helper. Then give Worksheet 13 as a second check.

ACTIVITIES:
Do Worksheet 13.
Read the directions. Let the children do the page independently.
Check together as review of concepts in sections 1 and 2.
Pictures should include the sun, wind, and water in the first set and animal energy, electricity, fuels, or solar energy in the second set.

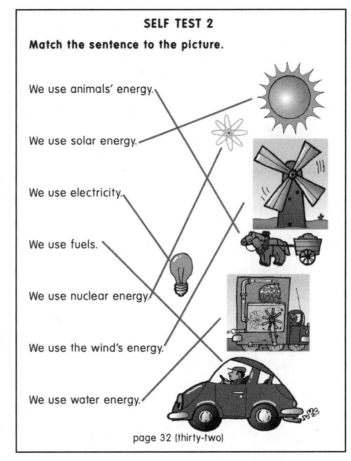

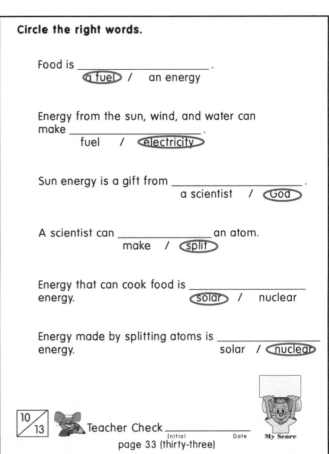

Name _____

Draw energy God gives us.

sun	wind	water

Draw energy we use.

animals other foods	gasoline coal	nuclear power electricity

Science: 108
Worksheet 13
with page 33

Teacher check _____
Initial   Date

Pages 34 and 35: We Save Energy

CONCEPTS:
God wants us to take care of the world He created.
We can help by saving energy.

OBJECTIVE: I can tell some ways to save energy.

PROCESSES: observing, predicting

READING INTEGRATION: main idea, following directions

VOCABULARY: (save)

MATERIALS NEEDED: word card (save), LIFEPAC Tablet, Worksheet 14, crayons, pencils

TEACHING PAGES 34 and 35:
Review the kinds of energy used by most people. Ask the children to tell the kinds of energy they use everyday and where it comes from.
Possible answers: electricity, gasoline (perhaps to get to school), gas, oil, electricity or coal for heat
Ask them to think of ways they might use less energy. Ask why it might be important to save energy (example: to save fuel).
Read the paragraphs to the class or have them read by volunteers.
Ask what Sunny is doing to save energy.
Ask for a volunteer to find and read the two direction sentences on page 35. Have the children complete the activities independently.
Allow time for the children to share their pictures and sentences.

ACTIVITY:
Do Worksheet 14.
Read the poem to the children.
Read it again and have them repeat
Have them clap the rhythm.
Read the direction.
When the children have finished, discuss the other ways to save energy.

III. WE SAVE ENERGY

God made the world.
God wants us to take care
of His world.

Sunny wants to help.
How about you?

page 34 (thirty-four)

Draw something you can do to save energy.

In your Tablet write a sentence telling how you can save energy.

page 35 (thirty-five)

Name _____

When the sun has gone to bed
It's, oh, so dark at night.
When you have to read or write,
Of course, you need some light.
but, when it's getting very late
and time to go to bed,
Please turn me off!
Don't leave me on!
Save energy, instead!

Follow the dots to see what to turn off to save energy.

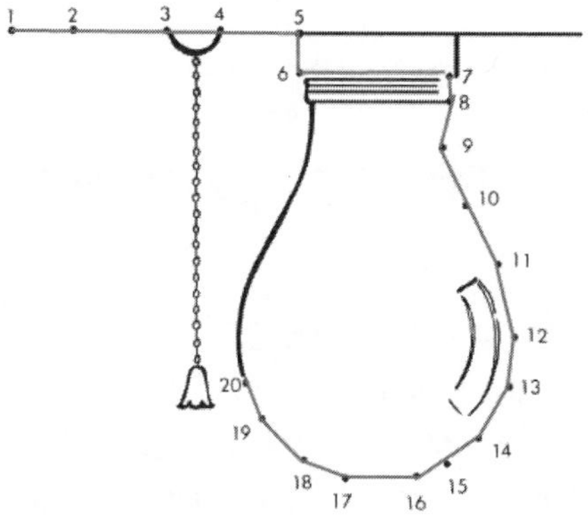

Science: 108
Worksheet 14
with page 35

Teacher check _____
Initial   Date

Pages 36 and 37: We Waste Fuel

CONCEPT: We waste fuels in many ways.

OBJECTIVE: I can tell some ways to save energy.

PROCESSES: observing, predicting

READING INTEGRATION: main idea, following directions, recalling details

VOCABULARY: waste, replaced

MATERIALS NEEDED: vocabulary word cards, pencils

TEACHING PAGES 36 and 37:

Present the vocabulary. Emphasize the meanings of waste and replace. *Waste:* to use or throw away something that has value. In case of energy, it is using our fuel supplies unnecessarily or in excess. *Replace:* to get again. A replaceable fuel is wood. Trees will grow again. Other energy sources cannot be replaced.

Read the text aloud or have it read by volunteers.

Discuss each energy use.

Example: Does it waste energy and fuel to drive a car or truck? Answer: Only if the trip is unnecessary. Ask the children to suggest some necessary and unnecessary uses of a car or truck. Follow the same procedure with heating and electricity uses.

Ask a child to find and read the direction sentence on page 37.

Have the children complete the activity independently.

Check the page together and discuss each picture.

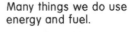

WE WASTE FUEL

Many things we do use energy and fuel.

Driving cars and trucks uses energy and fuel.

Heating our homes, schools, and churches uses energy and fuel.

Electricity uses energy and fuel.

Sometimes we use more fuel than we need. We waste fuel.

When we use fuel, we use it up. Some fuels cannot be replaced.

page 36 (thirty-six)

Circle things you do that waste fuel.

page 37 (thirty-seven)

Pages 38 and 39: Saving Energy

CONCEPT: Everyone can help to save energy.

OBJECTIVE: I can tell some ways to save energy.

PROCESSES: predicting, classifying

READING INTEGRATION: main idea, recalling detail

MATERIALS NEEDED: poster board, pencils, magazines, paste, scissors, paints or crayons, banner paper or tagboard

TEACHING PAGES 38 and 39:

Read the text to the children or have it read by a volunteer.

Discuss ways scientists, other grownups, and even children can help to save energy.

Ask a student to find and read the direction sentences.

Have the children complete the page independently, giving individual help as needed.

Check the page together and discuss each answer.

ACTIVITIES:

1. Provide tag board or banner paper for the children to make energy conservation posters. Also make available old magazines, paints, crayons, scissors, and glue. Let the children work in pairs. Display the posters in the classroom.

2. Have the children check back through the LIFEPAC to prepare for Self Test 3.

WE CAN SAVE ENERGY

Saving energy saves fuel.
Scientists can help.

Scientists can find
new ways to make energy.
Grown-ups can help.

YOU CAN HELP!

page 38 (thirty-eight)

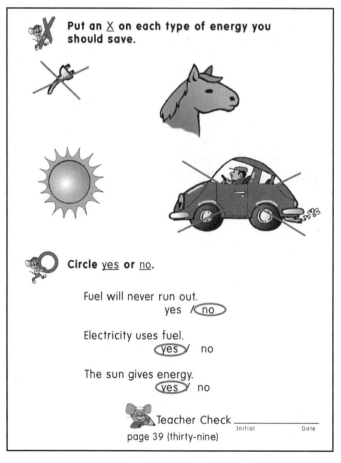

Put an X on each type of energy you should save.

Circle yes or no.

Fuel will never run out.
yes / no

Electricity uses fuel.
yes / no

The sun gives energy.
yes / no

Teacher Check _____
Initial   Date

page 39 (thirty-nine)

Page 40: Self Test 3

CONCEPT: evaluation

OBJECTIVES:
I can tell about energy God gives to us.
I can tell about energy we use.
I can tell about some ways to save energy.

READING INTEGRATION: following directions, recalling details

VOCABULARY: Review all the vocabulary.

MATERIALS NEEDED: pencils

TEACHING PAGE 40:
Review the vocabulary and concepts for the entire LIFEPAC, with special emphasis on section 3.

Read through the directions for the self test with the group. Answer any questions they might have.

The general proficiency of your group will dictate whether you choose to direct the self test or allow the children to proceed independently, once the directions are given.

In either case, you should be available to answer questions and to help with vocabulary, as needed.

For those children who need extra help, have them work with a classroom helper or a parent to prepare for the LIFEPAC Test.

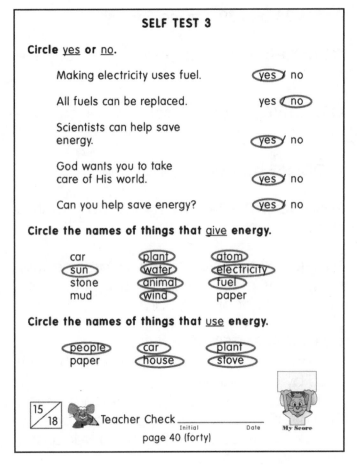

Page 41: Take Home Activity Page

MATERIALS NEEDED: crayons, scissors, construction paper, paste

TEACHING PAGE 41:

Have the children color the picture. Have them cut it out with the caption (Be an energy saver).

Have them paste the poster on construction paper and take it home to remind them to save energy.

LIFEPAC TEST AND ALTERNATE LIFEPAC TEST:

Administer the test to the class as a group. Ask to have directions read or read them to the class. In either case, be sure that the children clearly understand. Put examples on the board if it seems necessary. Give ample time for each activity to be completed before going on to the next.

Correct immediately and discuss with the child.

Review any concepts that have been missed.

Give those children who do not achieve the 80% score additional copies of the worksheets and a list of vocabulary words to study. A parent or a classroom helper should help in the review.

When the child is ready, give the Alternate LIFEPAC Test. Use the same procedure as for the LIFEPAC TEST.

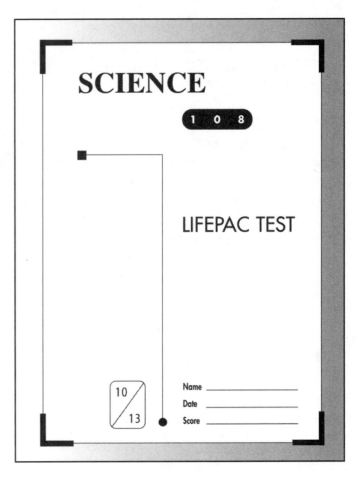

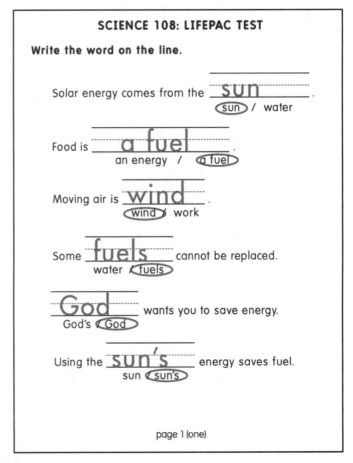

Match the picture with the fuel it uses.

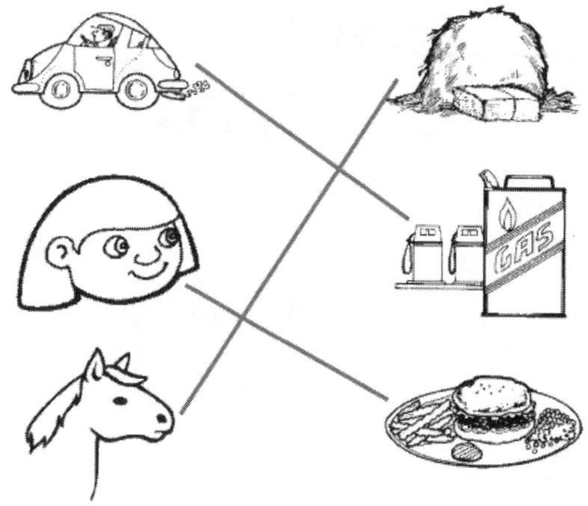

Read the sentence. Circle <u>fact</u> **or** <u>fantasy</u>.

Scientists can split atoms.
(fact) / fantasy

Trucks can fly.
fact / (fantasy)

page 2 (two)

Draw two ways you can help save energy.

page 3 (three)

SCIENCE

1 0 8

ALTERNATE LIFEPAC TEST

10/13

Name _____

Date _____

Score _____

SCIENCE 108: ALTERNATE LIFEPAC TEST

Circle the word.

Food is _____.
(fuel) / energy

Wind is moving _____.
water / (air)

You should _____ energy.
(save) / waste

Using the _____ energy saves fuel.
sun / (sun's)

Sun energy is called _____.
(solar) / water

God made _____ energy.
nuclear / (solar)

page 1 (one)

Circle fact or fantasy.

Scientists can split atoms.   (fact) / fantasy

Cows can fly.   fact / (fantasy)

Match the picture with the fuel.

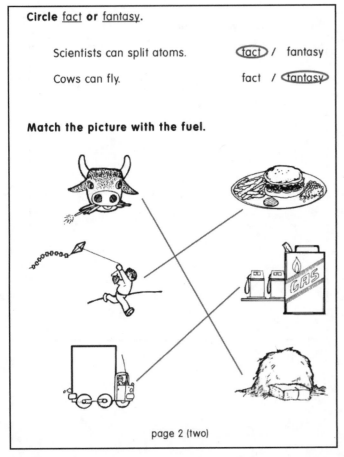

page 2 (two)

Draw two ways you can help save energy.

page 3 (three)

Pages 1 and 2: Machines Around You

CONCEPT: Simple machines make work easier.

OBJECTIVE: Introduction to the objectives of LIFEPAC 109.

BIBLE REFERENCE: John 1:1 through 5, John 1:3

PROCESSES: observing, comparing

READING INTEGRATION: main idea, rhyming

VOCABULARY: simple machine, lever, wheel, inclined plane, machine

MATERIALS NEEDED: vocabulary word cards, Bible

TEACHING PAGES 1 and 2

Present the vocabulary but do not expect the children to master *lever, wheel* or *inclined plane* at this time. These words will become familiar later in the LIFEPAC.

Read aloud from the Bible, John 1:1 through 5. The Bible tells us that without God nothing would have been made. Without God, men would not have been able to make simple machines.

Read the poem aloud to the children.

Ask them to volunteer the names of some machines with which they are familiar. They will probably mention sewing machines, washing machines and so on.

Tell them that the machines they will learn about in LIFEPAC 109 are ones they probably see every day, but do not think of as machines.

Discuss the illustration. Have the children name the simple machines in the pictures.

Read the objectives. Stress that these objectives are things the children will be able to do when LIFEPAC 109 is completed.

Have a volunteer read the statement and the question for discussion.

MACHINES AROUND YOU

Lift it up.
Push it down.
Turn the wheel
Around and around.
Whatever the work
That you do,
A simple machine
Makes it easy for you.

Objectives

1. I can tell about some levers.
2. I can tell about some wheels.
3. I can tell about some inclined planes.

page 1 (one)

Here are some simple machines. Tell what work they help you do.

page 2 (two)

Give the children time to look at the pictures and think about the purpose of each simple machine.

Ask for volunteers to tell about the machines.

ACTIVITIES:

1.   Prepare a table with books about simple machines.

2.   In your discovery center place a number of simple machines commonly found around the house. Give the children an opportunity to experiment with them throughout the unit.

3.   Have the children memorize John 1:3.

Page 3: Activity Page

MATERIALS NEEDED: LIFEPAC Tablet, pencils, crayons

TEACHING PAGE 3:

Have a volunteer read the direction.

When the children understand what to do, have them complete the page independently.

When the activity has been completed have each child tell about his picture.

ACTIVITY:

Each child should write a sentence about his picture in his Tablet. Give individual help with spelling, as needed. More capable students should write a paragraph or two.

Simple machine—a basic mechanical device which increases force or changes its direction. The lever, wedge, and screw are simple machines.

Draw something you can do with a simple machine.

page 3 (three)

I. PART ONE

Page 4: Levers

CONCEPTS:
A lever is a simple machine.
We use levers every day.

OBJECTIVE: I can tell about some levers.

PROCESS: observing.

READING INTEGRATION: main idea, rhyming, speaking in a group

VOCABULARY: lever, open, toolbox, kitchen

MATERIALS NEEDED: vocabulary word cards, pictures of levers

TEACHING PAGE 4:
Present the vocabulary.
Read the poem aloud to the class. Reread it. Have the children listen for and identify the vocabulary words and the rhyming words.
Read the poem a third time with the children following along.
Ask for a volunteer to read the question for discussion. Allow time for the children to name and discuss levers they know. Have them find these simple levers in the discovery center.

Lever—a bar or board used for lifting a weight at one end by pushing down at the other end.

I. LEVERS

To open a can
Or fill a pail,
To crack a nut
Or pull a nail,

Do you know
What you should use?
A lever is
The one to choose.

A lever is a simple machine.

 Can you name some levers you might find in the kitchen or in a toolbox?

page 4 (four)

Page 5: Activity Page

MATERIALS NEEDED: pencils, crayons

TEACHING PAGE 5:

Ask a volunteer to read the direction sentence.

When the children understand what to do, have them complete the page independently. They may also color the picture.

Give the children an opportunity to tell about the picture.

Note: a teeter-totter is a lever in that it works by a force lifting a load with the help of a fulcrum. The force and the load change places as the ends are moved up and down.

ACTIVITY:

Use the playground teeter-totter or make one with a sawhorse and a long board. Experiment by moving the board into different positions. Have the children of different weights try the different positions.

Show how a light weight child can lift a heavy one (or the teacher) by increasing the length of the force side of the board.

Follow the dots to see a lever you can ride.

page 5 (five)

Page 6: Levers

CONCEPT: Levers help make work easy.

OBJECTIVE: I can tell about some levers.

PROCESSES: observing, comparing

READING INTEGRATION: main idea, vocabulary development

VOCABULARY: cover, nail, rock, stuck

MATERIALS NEEDED: knife or bottle opener, jar with a pry-off lid, hammer, nail, board, large rock (about 10 lbs.), small rock, stick, vocabulary word cards, LIFEPAC Tablet

TEACHING PAGE 6:

Present the vocabulary words. Match the words with the corresponding objects.

Read the sentences aloud or have them read by volunteers.

Using the materials listed let the children test the situations pictured on the page.

Ask a child to try to move the rock with his hands then with the stick as a lever. "Which is easier?"

Hammer the nail part way into the board. Have a child try to remove it, first with fingers, then with hammer claw. "Which is easier?"

Repeat with a lidded jar. "Which is easier?"

Provide discussion time to explore other ways levers make work easy.

ACTIVITY:

Have the children write this sentence in their Tablets:

Levers help make work easy.

SOME SIMPLE LEVERS

The rock is too big.

A lever can help.

The nail is stuck.

A lever can help.

The cover is too tight.

A lever can help.

page 6 (six)

Page 7: Activity Page

MATERIALS NEEDED: pencils, Worksheet 1

TEACHING PAGE 7:

Ask for volunteers to read the statements and the direction sentences.

When the children understand what to do have them complete the page independently. Give individual help as needed.

Check the page together.

ACTIVITY:

Do Worksheet 1.

Read the direction. Have the children identify each picture. Ask what they would use to do each job.

Have the children finish the page.

Check by having each child tell what he has drawn and why.

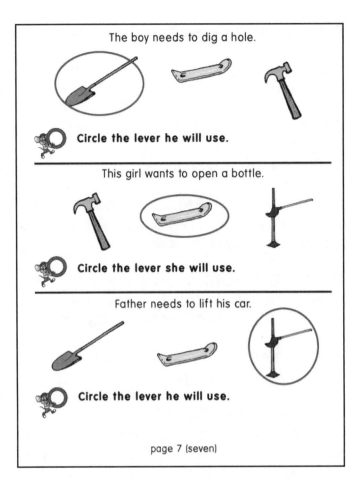

The boy needs to dig a hole.

Circle the lever he will use.

This girl wants to open a bottle.

Circle the lever she will use.

Father needs to lift his car.

Circle the lever he will use.

page 7 (seven)

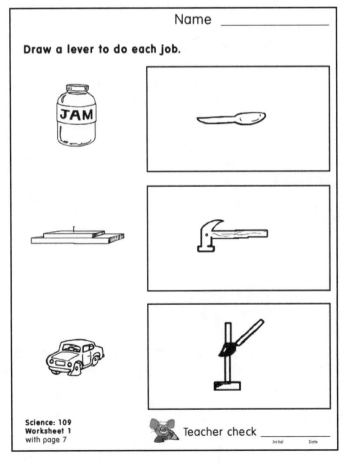

Name _____

Draw a lever to do each job.

JAM

Science: 109
Worksheet 1
with page 7

Teacher check _____
Initial   Date

Pages 8 and 9: Levers Work Together

CONCEPT: Some tools we use are made of two levers working together.

OBJECTIVE: I can tell about some levers.

PROCESSES: observing, predicting

READING INTEGRATION: main idea, vocabulary development, speaking in a group, following directions

MATERIALS NEEDED: vocabulary word cards scissors, pliers, nutcrackers, other tools made of levers, Worksheet 2, pencils, crayons

VOCABULARY: Tool, scissors, pliers, nutcracker, clippers (pair)

TEACHING PAGES 8 and 9:
Present the vocabulary. Match the words with the objects they represent.

Read the title and the statements at the top of the page or have them read by volunteers.

Ask the children to identify the tools pictured.

Proceed with the discussion question. Have the children try to think of other tools made with two levers (scissors of assorted sizes, hedge clippers, tongs, bellows).

Have a volunteer read the direction sentence on page 9.

Have the children complete the activity independently. Check it together.

ACTIVITY:
Do Worksheet 2.
Read the directions.
Discuss the picture. Have the children circle the levers.

Check together by having the children tell why each tool they circled is a lever.

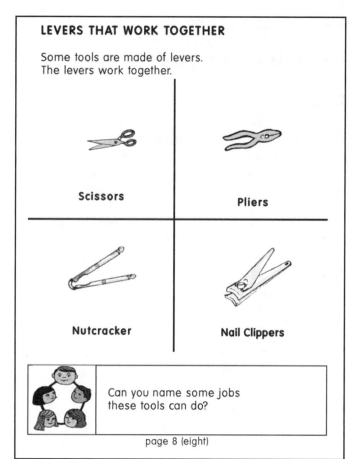

LEVERS THAT WORK TOGETHER

Some tools are made of levers. The levers work together.

Scissors

Pliers

Nutcracker

Nail Clippers

Can you name some jobs these tools can do?

page 8 (eight)

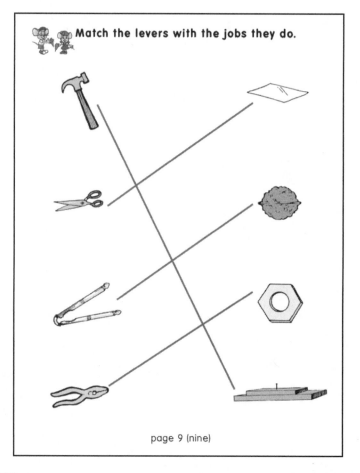

Match the levers with the jobs they do.

page 9 (nine)

Name _____

Circle the tools made of levers.
Color the picture.

Science: 109
Worksheet 2
with page 9

Teacher check _____
                                    Initial   Date

165

Page 10: How Levers Work

CONCEPT: Levers work by a force moving a load using a fulcrum.

OBJECTIVE: I can tell about some levers.

PROCESSES: observing, classifying

READING INTEGRATION: main idea, recalling detail

VOCABULARY: force, fulcrum, load

MATERIALS NEEDED: vocabulary word cards, pictures of assorted levers (to use in identifying force, fulcrum, and load), LIFEPAC Tablet

TEACHING PAGE 10:

Read the statements to the class. Identify each part as you go.

For the force, show how the boy has to work to make the lever move down.

The fulcrum is necessary to provide a point where the direction of movement of the lever changes from down to up.

Demonstrate with the stick and stones used for page 6.

Discussion: Give the children an opportunity to identify the force, fulcrum, and load of the teeter-totter, the pump, and any other levers they may know about.

ACTIVITY:

Have the children write these sentences in their Tablets.

A lever needs a force.
A lever needs a fulcrum.
A lever moves a load.

HOW LEVERS WORK

A lever needs a force.
The boy is the force.

A lever moves a load.
The rock is the load.

A lever needs a fulcrum.
The log is the fulcrum.

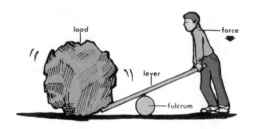

 Can you show the force, the load, and the fulcrum on a teeter-totter or on a pump?

page 10 (ten)

Page 11: Activity Page

VOCABULARY: fisherman, oar, oarlock

MATERIALS NEEDED: vocabulary word cards, pictures representing the words, pencils, Worksheet 3, crayons

TEACHING PAGE 11:

Introduce the vocabulary. Match the words to the pictures.

Ask a volunteer to find and read the direction sentences.

Review the vocabulary words by finding them as labels on the picture.

Have the children complete the page independently, giving individual help as needed.

Check it together by having the children identify the part of the picture that goes with each sentence.

ACTIVITY:

Do Worksheet 3.

Discuss the illustration.

Have the children explain the labels and the operation of the wheelbarrow.

Look at the picture.

fisherman (force)

oarlock (fulcrum)

oar (lever)

water (load)

Write the words.

fisherman   oar   water   oarlock

The ___oar___ is a lever.

The ___fisherman___ is the force.

The ___water___ is the load.

The ___oarlock___ is the fulcrum.

page 11 (eleven)

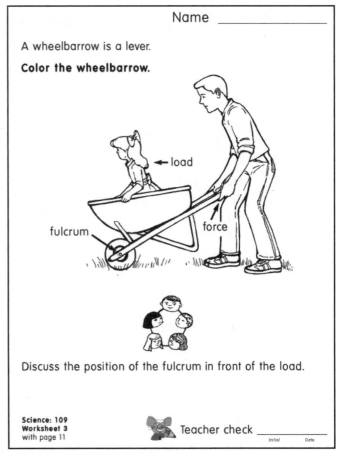

Name _____

A wheelbarrow is a lever.

Color the wheelbarrow.

← load

fulcrum

force

Discuss the position of the fulcrum in front of the load.

Science: 109
Worksheet 3
with page 11

Teacher check _____
Initial   Date

Pages 12 and 13: Self Test 1

CONCEPT: evaluation

OBJECTIVE: I can tell about some levers.

READING INTEGRATION: following directions, recalling details

VOCABULARY: Review all the vocabulary.

MATERIALS NEEDED: pencils, Worksheet 4

TEACHING PAGES 12 and 13:
Review the vocabulary words from section 1.

Practice matching words to pictures when it is possible.

Read all directions with the children. Be sure they are understood.

The general proficiency of your group should dictate whether you choose to direct the self test or allow the children to proceed independently, once directions are given.

In either case you should be available to answer questions and to help with the vocabulary as needed.

Check immediately. Review any concepts missed.

ACTIVITY:
Do Worksheet 4.

Read the direction.

Let the children complete the page independently.

Check by having the child tell you what he circled and why.

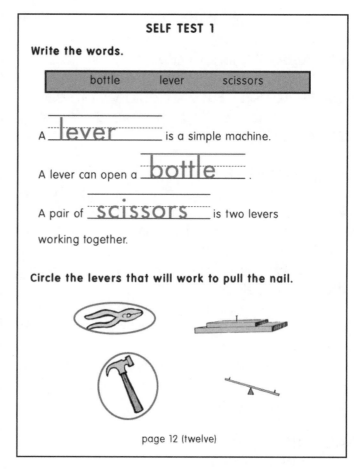

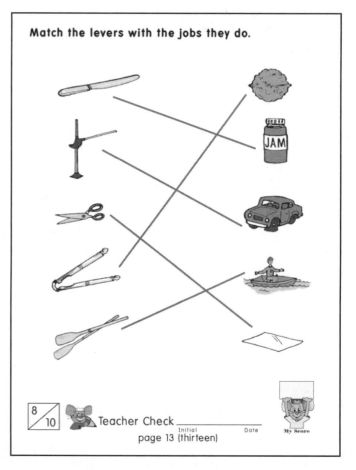

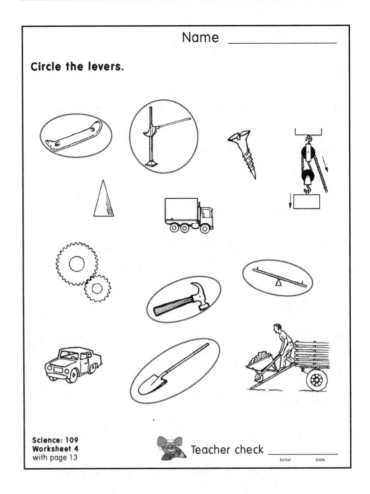

Name _____

Circle the levers.

Science: 109
Worksheet 4
with page 13

Teacher check _____
Initial   Date

II. PART TWO

Page 14: Wheels

CONCEPT: A wheel is a simple machine.

OBJECTIVE I can tell about some wheels.

BIBLE REFERENCE:
Wheels were used in Biblical times.
See these references: Exodus 14:25; Psalm 83:13; Proverbs 20:26; Ezekiel 1:16, 10:9, 10, 12, 13; Daniel 7:9; Nahum 3:2.

PROCESS: observing

READING INTEGRATION: main idea, rhyming, speaking in a group

VOCABULARY: wheel

MATERIALS NEEDED: vocabulary word card, pictures of all kinds and sizes of wheels, LIFEPAC Tablet, drawing paper, crayons

TEACHING PAGE 14:
Introduce the section by presenting the vocabulary word. Provide discussion time for the children to tell about wheels.

Tell that the wheel has been used to make work easier for a very long time. Refer to Bible mention of wheels.

Read the poem aloud.

Have the children think of other ways wheels help.

You may want the children to draw pictures of wheels at work.

ACTIVITY:
Have the children write this sentence in their Tablets.

A wheel is a simple machine.

II. WHEELS

Without the **wheel**
Things bump and bounce
And drag along the ground.
Without the wheel
No bikes or cars
Or trucks could move around.
Without the wheel
No clocks would tick
Or flags slide up a pole.
Aren't you glad
We have the wheel
To make so many things go?

A wheel is a simple machine.

page 14 (fourteen)

Page 15 : Activity Page

VOCABULARY: horse, wagon

MATERIALS NEEDED: crayons

TEACHING PAGE 15:

Have a volunteer read the question. Ask the children to look at the picture and decide what is missing. (The wagon has no wheels.)

Ask how wheels would make the horse's work easier.

Have a volunteer find and read the direction sentences.

When the directions are understood have the children complete the page independently.

Give the children time to show their pictures.

What will help the horse pull the wagon?

Draw some things that will help. Color the picture.

page 15 (fifteen)

Pages 16 and 17: Wheels

CONCEPT: Wheels help things move.

OBJECTIVE: I can tell about some wheels.

PROCESSES: observing, classifying

READING INTEGRATION: main idea, speaking in a group, following directions

VOCABULARY: easier

MATERIALS NEEDED: pictures of things that move on wheels and small replicas of those objects (examples: toy cars, trucks, tinker toys), pencils, Worksheet 5

TEACHING PAGES 16 and 17:

Have a volunteer read the page title, the picture captions, and the discussion question.

Give the children an opportunity to study the pictures and to answer these questions:

"What makes the work easier?"

"Where did the wheels come from?"

"How do you think the children managed to put the wheels under the large box?" (They might have used a lever.)

Discussion question: Have the children name some familiar objects that have wheels. Have the pictures and replicas of wheeled vehicles available for the discussion.

Play a matching game with the wheels and the corresponding vehicles.

Ask for a volunteer to read the direction sentence on page 17.

Have the children complete the page independently.

Check it together and have the children tell how they knew which wheels matched the object (size, number, and so on).

ACTIVITY:

Do Worksheet 5.

Have a child read the directions.

WHEELS

Wheels are machines.
Wheels help things move.
Wheels make work easier.

What would make this work easier?

Wheels help make work easier.

Can you tell about some wheels that help things move?

page 16 (sixteen)

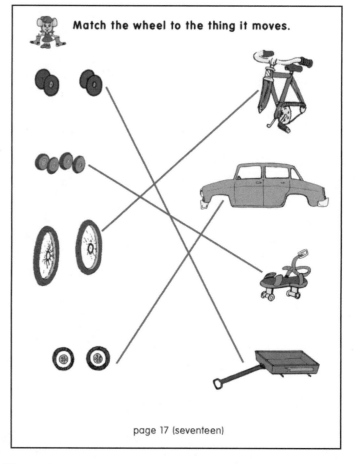

Match the wheel to the thing it moves.

page 17 (seventeen)

After the children finish their drawings, allow time for each child to tell about his pictures.

Name _____

**Draw four things with wheels.
Color your pictures.**

Science: 109
Worksheet 5
with page 17

Teacher check _____
Initial   Date

Pages 18 and 19: Gears

CONCEPTS: Gears are wheels with teeth. They make work easier.

OBJECTIVE: I can tell about some wheels.

PROCESSES: observing, comparing, classifying

READING INTEGRATION: picture interpretation, main idea, following directions, recalling details

VOCABULARY: teeth, gear, easily, turn, (fast)

MATERIALS NEEDED: clock with gears exposed (if available), commercial gear game, pictures of machines that have visible gears, egg beater, crayons, LIFEPAC Tablet, Worksheet 6

TEACHING PAGES 18 and 19:

With the gear game, clock, and so on, demonstrate how interlocking gears work together to run more complicated machines.

Read the picture captions to the children or have them read by volunteers.

Ask the children to find and point out the gears in each picture.

Give the children a chance to handle and learn about the gears in the egg beater.

Ask a volunteer to identify and read the three direction sentences on page 19.

When the children understand what to do have them complete the page independently. Give individual help as needed.

Check the page together.

ACTIVITIES:

1.   Have the children write this sentence in their Tablets. Gears are wheels with teeth.

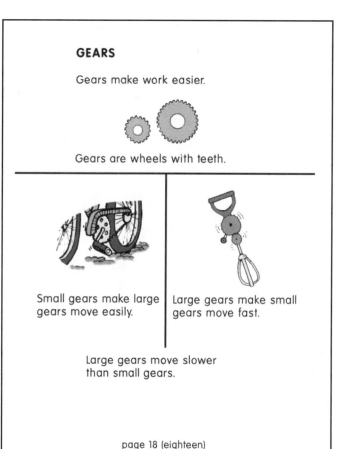

GEARS

Gears make work easier.

Gears are wheels with teeth.

Small gears make large gears move easily.

Large gears make small gears move fast.

Large gears move slower than small gears.

page 18 (eighteen)

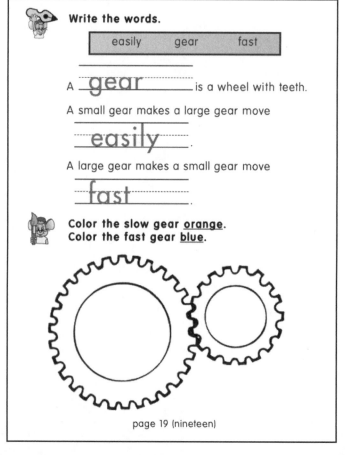

Write the words.

easily	gear	fast

A ___gear___ is a wheel with teeth.

A small gear makes a large gear move

___easily___ .

A large gear makes a small gear move

___fast___ .

Color the slow gear orange.
Color the fast gear blue.

page 19 (nineteen)

2.   Do Worksheet 6.

Read the directions.

Have the children look at the egg beater and other objects or pictures with gears.

Let them complete the page. Check to see that the gears drawn by the children actually mesh with the two gears on the page. If they do not, point out the meshing gears on the egg beater and have the child correct his illustration.

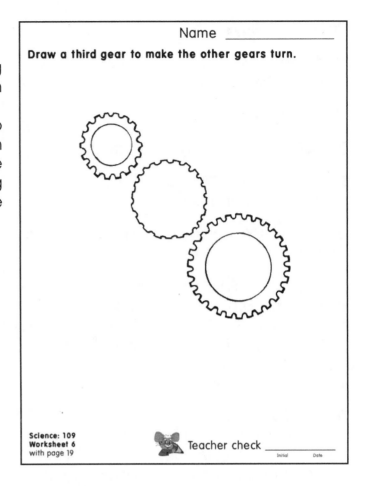

Name _____

Draw a third gear to make the other gears turn.

Science: 109
Worksheet 6
with page 19

Teacher check _____
Initial   Date

Page 20: Pulleys

CONCEPT: Pulleys are wheels that work with rope to lift and move things.

OBJECTIVE: I can tell about some wheels.

PROCESSES: observing, comparing

READING INTEGRATION: main ideas, interpreting illustrations

VOCABULARY: pulley, rope, lift, back, forth, heavy

MATERIALS NEEDED: pulleys to use in the classroom both for lifting and for moving things across the room, clothespins, vocabulary word cards to match with parts and action of pulley, LIFEPAC Tablet, crayons, Worksheet 7

TEACHING PAGE 20:

Present the vocabulary and concepts by demonstrating the use of pulleys to lift an object and to move objects back and forth. Match the pulleys, their parts (wheels and ropes), and their actions with the words.

Read the statements and the captions to the class, or have them read by volunteers.

Give the children time to study the pictures. Provide the opportunity for them to tell how the pulley makes work easier in each illustration. Have them demonstrate how the clothesline works by clipping messages to the line and having children send their messages from one side to the next.

ACTIVITIES:

1. Have the children write the picture captions in their Tablets.
2. Do Worksheet 7.
   Read the direction.
   After the children circle the pulleys, talk about the illustration. Have the children tell how each pulley is helping.
   Have the children color the picture.

PULLEYS

Pulleys are wheels.
Pulleys work with ropes.

Pulleys help to lift heavy things.

Pulleys help move things back and forth.

page 20 (twenty)

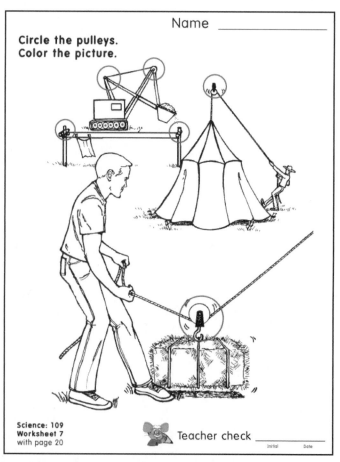

Name _____

**Circle the pulleys.
Color the picture.**

Science: 109
Worksheet 7
with page 20

Teacher check _____
Initial   Date

Page 21: Activity Page

MATERIALS NEEDED: crayons, pencils, pulleys

TEACHING PAGE 21:

Review the vocabulary words in the box and concepts presented.

Ask a volunteer to identify and read the direction sentences.

Have the children complete the page independently, giving individual help as needed.

Check the page together. Give the children a chance to share their pictures and tell what the pulley (block and tackle) is helping to lift.

Let the children demonstrate how a block and tackle works by using it to lift a chair, some books, or some other object.

Follow the dots.
Color the picture.

What is the pulley helping to lift?

Write the words.

| gears | move | pulleys |

Wheels help things ___move___ .

Wheels that work with ropes are ___pulleys___ .

Wheels with teeth are ___gears___ .

page 21 (twenty-one)

Pages 22 and 23: Self Test 2

CONCEPT: evaluation

OBJECTIVES:
I can tell about some levers.
I can tell about some wheels.

READING INTEGRATION: following directions, recalling details

VOCABULARY: Review all the vocabulary words.

MATERIALS NEEDED: pencils, Worksheet 8

TEACHING PAGES 22 and 23:
Review vocabulary and concepts for sections 1 and 2.

Read all the directions with the children. Be sure they are understood.

The general proficiency of your group will dictate whether you choose to direct the self test or allow the children to proceed independently, once directions are given.

In either case you should be available to answer questions and help with vocabulary, as needed.

Check immediately. Go over the test with each child.

Have the children who need the review go over the first two sections with their parents or a classroom helper. Give Worksheet 8 as a second check.

ACTIVITY:
Do Worksheet 8.

Read the direction. Have the children do the page independently.

Check individually by asking each child to identity each item, tell what it is (wheel or lever), and what it does. Use this checking process to review the concepts taught in the first two sections.

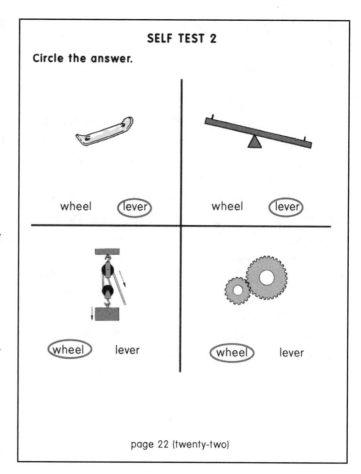

SELF TEST 2

Circle the answer.

wheel (lever)   wheel (lever)

(wheel) lever   (wheel) lever

page 22 (twenty-two)

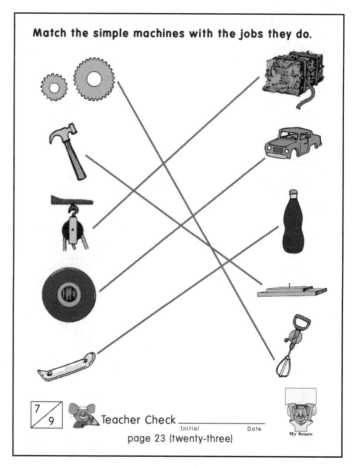

Match the simple machines with the jobs they do.

7/9 Teacher Check _____
Initial   Date
page 23 (twenty-three)

Name _____

Write <u>L</u> **on the levers.**
Write <u>W</u> **on the wheels.**

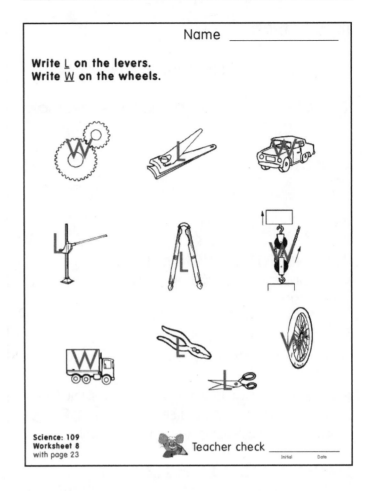

Science: 109
Worksheet 8
with page 23

Teacher check _____

Initial   Date

III. PART THREE

Pages 24 and 25: Inclined Planes

CONCEPT: An inclined plane is a simple machine.

OBJECTIVE: I can tell about some inclined planes.

PROCESS: observing

READING INTEGRATION: main idea, rhyming, vocabulary development, following directions

VOCABULARY: inclined plane, screw, wedge, smooth, easy, metal

MATERIALS: vocabulary word cards, pictures representing vocabulary, piece of tag board or cardboard, crayons, pencils

TEACHING PAGES 24 and 25:

Present the vocabulary. Stress that a plane is a flat surface. Inclined means to be tilted or at an angle. Demonstrate with the tag board. Show that the tag is a flat surface, a plane. When it is tipped up like a ramp it becomes an inclined plane.

Read the poem aloud.

Ask the children to listen for kinds of inclined planes and for rhyming words. Reread the poem. Then have the children read it with you.

Spend a little time identifying the inclined planes in the illustration.

Ask for a volunteer to read the statement and the instruction sentence on page 25.

Have the children complete the page independently They may also color the picture.

When all have finished, allow time to share the pictures.

III. INCLINED PLANES

Up so easy and
Down so smooth,
An inclined plane
Helps you move.

Turn it around,
A metal rod,
You have a screw
To do a job.

Put two together
You make a wedge
To chop some wood
Or trim a hedge.

That simple machine,
The inclined plane,
Can help a lot
In many ways.

page 24 (twenty-four)

This inclined plane helps you play.

Follow the dots to see.

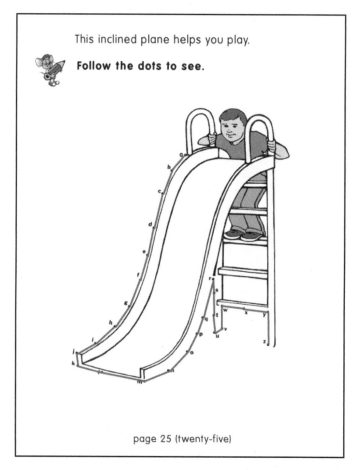

page 25 (twenty-five)

Page 26: Ramps

CONCEPT: A ramp is an inclined plane that helps things move easily.

OBJECTIVE: I can tell about some inclined planes.

PROCESS: observing

READING INTEGRATION: main idea, identifying a problem and a solution, interpreting illustrations

VOCABULARY: ramp, wheelchair

MATERIALS NEEDED: LIFEPAC Tablet

TEACHING PAGE 26:
Read the captions aloud to the class or have them read by a volunteer.

Ask the children to identify the problem in the first picture. (The wheelchair cannot go up the steps.)

Have them explain how the problem was solved. (The steps were replaced by a ramp, an inclined plane.)

ACTIVITY:
Have the children write this sentence in their Tablets:

A ramp is an inclined plane.

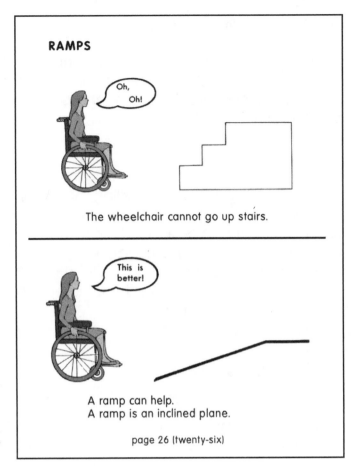

Page 27: Activity Page

MATERIALS NEEDED: pictures of inclined planes in use (bridges, ramps in parking garages, ramps into buildings, and so on), pencils, Worksheet 9, crayons

TEACHING PAGE 27:

Use the pictures to show how inclined planes are used in the building of roads, bridges, and buildings. Inclined planes are found in many places and are used in place of stairs where handicapped people might need to get in and out.

Ask a volunteer to read the direction sentence.

Have the children complete the page independently.

Check it together.

ACTIVITY:

Do Worksheet 9.

Have a child read the sentence and the direction.

Let the children do the page independently.

Check by having the child explain how he solved the problem by using an inclined plane. Let the other children decide whether the child's solution will work. If the child has not solved the problem correctly, have him correct his picture.

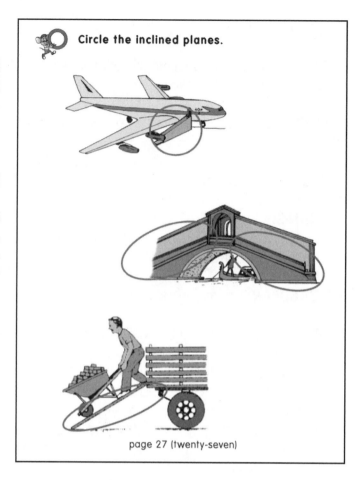

Circle the inclined planes.

page 27 (twenty-seven)

Name _____

The boy wants to take his wagon over the log. **Draw** <u>inclined planes</u> **that will help.**

Science: 109
Worksheet 9
with page 27

Teacher check _____
Initial   Date

Pages 28 and 29: Screws

CONCEPTS: A screw is an inclined plane. The plane goes up and around the screw and helps to hold things tight.

OBJECTIVE: I can tell about some inclined planes.

PROCESSES: observing, comparing, predicting

READING INTEGRATION: vocabulary development, main idea, speaking in a group, sequence, following directions

VOCABULARY: screw, tight, screwdriver

MATERIALS NEEDED: vocabulary word cards; assorted types and sizes of screws, bolts, and nuts; LIFEPAC Tablet; Worksheet 10; pencils

TEACHING PAGES 28 and 29:

Give the children an opportunity to handle the screws, to examine them carefully, and to see how the narrow plane winds up and around the metal.

Ask the children how they think the screw can hold things tight. (The inclined plane bites into the wood or other material and cannot be pulled straight out as a nail can.)

Read the statements aloud to the class or have them read by volunteers.

Discuss the diagram of a screw and its uses, as pictured on the page.

Discussion question: Give the children a chance to tell about places they have seen a screw being used.

Ask for a volunteer to read the directions at the top of page 29. Have the children complete the activity independently.

Check it together.

Discussion question: A screwdriver is a form of a lever. The force in this case is the turn of the handle. The fulcrum is the point at which the screwdriver meets the screw.

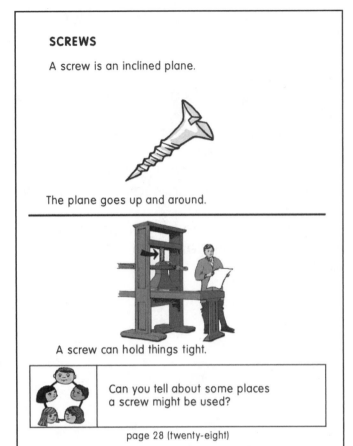

SCREWS

A screw is an inclined plane.

The plane goes up and around.

A screw can hold things tight.

Can you tell about some places a screw might be used?

page 28 (twenty-eight)

**Look at the picture story.
Write 1, 2, 3 to show what happened first, second, and third.**

What kind of simple machine is the screwdriver?

page 29 (twenty-nine)

The *load* is the screw being loosened or tightened.

ACTIVITIES:

1.   Have the children write this sentence in their tablets.

A screw is an inclined plane.

2.   Do Worksheet 10.

Read the directions. Make sure the children know what they are expected to do.

Let them finish the page independently.

Check together and discuss the illustrations.

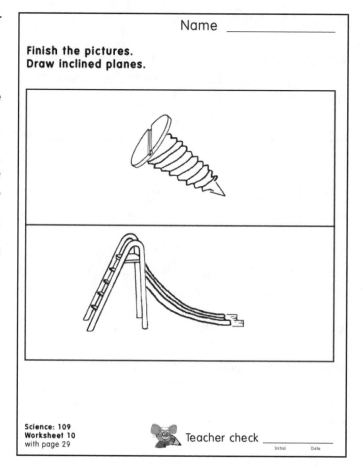

Name _____

Finish the pictures.
Draw inclined planes.

Science: 109
Worksheet 10
with page 29

Teacher check _____
Initial   Date

Pages 30 and 31: Wedges

CONCEPTS: Two inclined planes make a wedge. Wedges make work easier.

OBJECTIVE: I can tell about some inclined planes.

PROCESSES: observing, comparing

READING INTEGRATION: vocabulary development, main idea, following directions, speaking in a group, recalling details

VOCABULARY: wedge, ax, chop, knife, nail, doorstop, hedge

MATERIALS NEEDED: vocabulary word cards, objects or pictures representing vocabulary and other wedges, pencils

TEACHING PAGES 30 and 31:

Present the vocabulary. Use the pictures to compare the position of the inclined planes on various wedge type tools.

Example: The planes on a nail have a wider angle than the planes on a knife edge. This angle is too wide!

Read the statements and the picture captions to the class, or have them read by volunteers.

Give the children an opportunity to compare and discuss the wedges on the page.

Ask for a volunteer to read the direction sentence on page 31.

Have the children complete the activity independently.

Check it together.

Discussion question: The sharp edges of a hedge trimmer are inclined planes (wedges). Cutting tools have wedged edges (scissors, lawn mowers, hatchets, sickles, and so on).

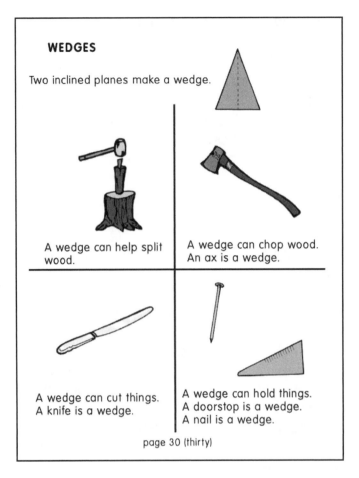

WEDGES

Two inclined planes make a wedge.

A wedge can help split wood.

A wedge can chop wood. An ax is a wedge.

A wedge can cut things. A knife is a wedge.

A wedge can hold things. A doorstop is a wedge. A nail is a wedge.

page 30 (thirty)

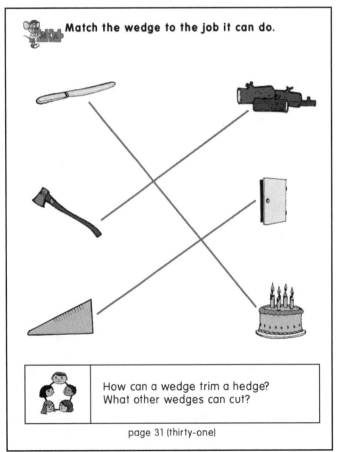

Match the wedge to the job it can do.

How can a wedge trim a hedge? What other wedges can cut?

page 31 (thirty-one)

185

Pages 32 and 33: Self Test 3

CONCEPT: evaluation

OBJECTIVES:
I can tell about some levers.
I can tell about some wheels.
I can tell about some inclined planes.

READING INTEGRATION: following directions, recalling details

VOCABULARY: Review all the vocabulary words.

MATERIALS NEEDED: pencils, Worksheet 11

TEACHING PAGES 32 and 33:

Review the vocabulary and concepts for the entire LIFEPAC, with special emphasis on section 3.

Read through the directions for the self test with the group. Answer any questions they might have.

The general proficiency of your group will dictate whether you choose to direct the self test or allow the children to proceed independently, once directions are given.

In either case, you should be available to answer questions and to help with vocabulary, as needed.

Check together immediately. Go over the test with each child. Review the concepts missed.

Provide Worksheet 11 for review.

For those children who need extra help, have them work with a classroom helper or a parent to prepare for the LIFEPAC Test.

ACTIVITY:

Do Worksheet 11.

Read the direction. Have the children do the page independently.

Check together and discuss as a review for the LIFEPAC Test.

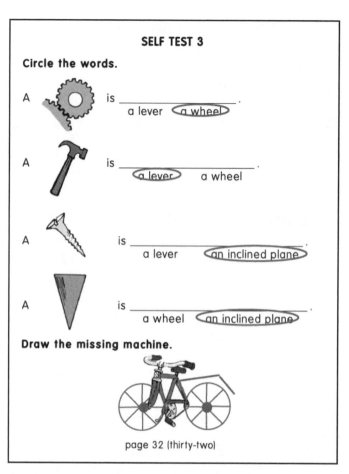

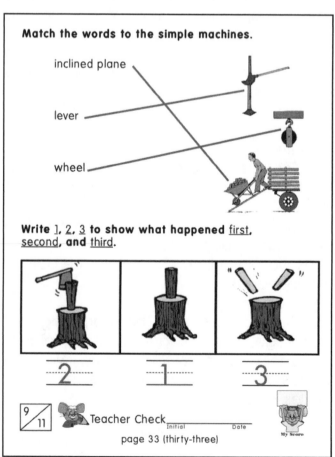

186

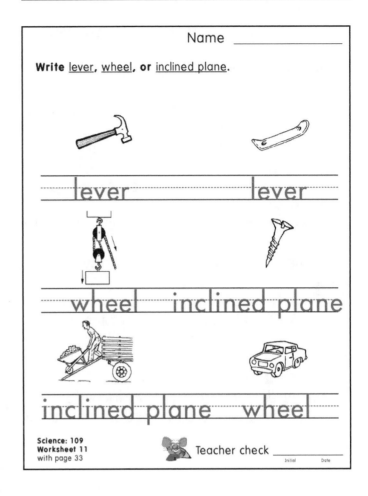

Name _____

Write <u>lever</u>, <u>wheel</u>, **or** <u>inclined plane</u>.

lever   lever

wheel   inclined plane

inclined plane   wheel

Science: 109
Worksheet 11
with page 33

Teacher check _____
Initial   Date

187

LIFEPAC TEST AND ALTERNATE LIFEPAC TEST:

Administer the test to the class as a group. Ask to have directions read or read them to the class. In either case, be sure that the children clearly understand. Put examples on the board if it seems necessary. Give ample time for each activity to be completed before going on to the next.

Correct immediately and discuss with the child.

Review any concepts that have been missed.

Give those children who do not achieve the 80% score additional copies of the worksheets and a list of vocabulary words to study. A parent or a classroom helper should help in the review.

When the child is ready, give the Alternate LIFEPAC Test. Use the same procedure as for the LIFEPAC TEST.

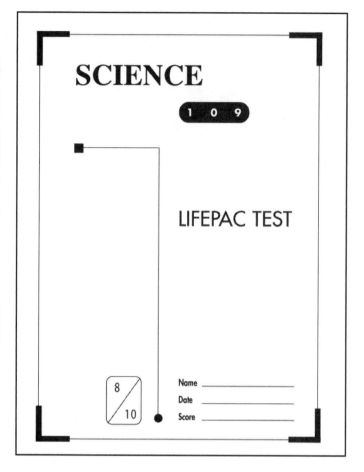

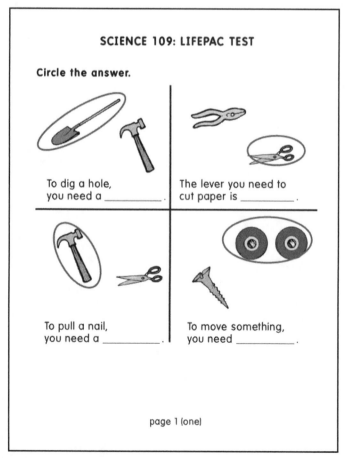

SCIENCE 109: LIFEPAC TEST

Circle the answer.

To dig a hole, you need a _____ .

The lever you need to cut paper is _____ .

To pull a nail, you need a _____ .

To move something, you need _____ .

page 1 (one)

Circle the levers.

Circle the wheels.

Circle the inclined planes.

page 2 (two)

NOTES

page 3 (three)

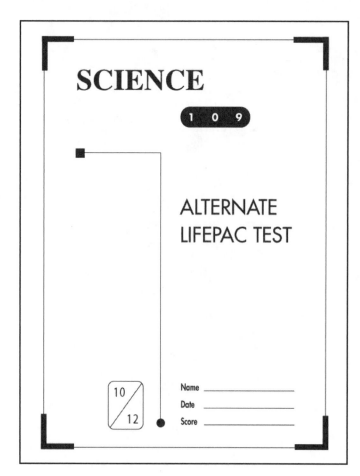

SCIENCE

1 0 9

ALTERNATE LIFEPAC TEST

10/12

Name _____
Date _____
Score _____

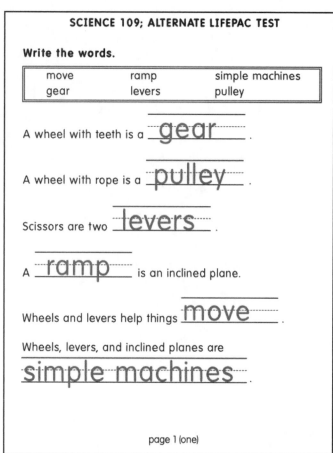

SCIENCE 109; ALTERNATE LIFEPAC TEST

Write the words.

move	ramp	simple machines
gear	levers	pulley

A wheel with teeth is a _gear_ .

A wheel with rope is a _pulley_ .

Scissors are two _levers_ .

A _ramp_ is an inclined plane.

Wheels and levers help things _move_ .

Wheels, levers, and inclined planes are _simple machines_ .

page 1 (one)

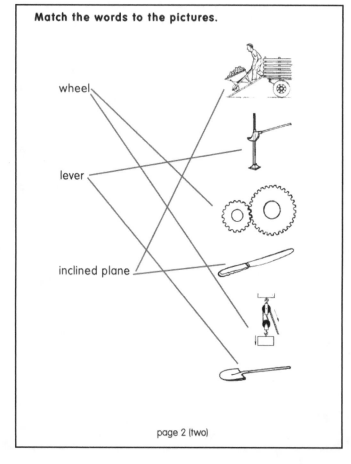

Match the words to the pictures.

wheel

lever

inclined plane

page 2 (two)

NOTES

page 3 (three)

Page 1: Wonderful World of Science

CONCEPT: Science is a way to learn about the world in which we live.

OBJECTIVE: An introduction to all of the objectives in LIFEPAC 110.

PROCESSES: observing, comparing, classifying, and predicting

READING INTEGRATION: main idea, speaking in a group

VOCABULARY: (observe, earth, living, myself, science)

MATERIALS NEEDED: LIFEPAC Tablet, pencil

TEACHING PAGE 1:

Read the introductory paragraph aloud to the class or have it read by volunteers.

Give the children an opportunity to recall and discuss the science units studied.

Read the objectives to the student. Make it clear that these are things they will be able to do when LIFEPAC 110 has been completed.

ACTIVITY:

Have the children write these sentences in their LIFEPAC Tablets:

Science helps me learn about the earth.

Science helps me learn about living things.

Science helps me learn about myself.

WONDERFUL WORLD OF SCIENCE

Science is fun.
In science I learn to observe
the world around me.
I learn about the earth.
I learn about living things.
I learn about myself.

 Objectives

1. I can tell about things I see, hear, smell, taste, and feel.

2. I can show how things I observe are alike and different.

3. I can tell how things I observe will grow or change.

4. I can tell ways my love will make the world better.

page 1 (one)

I. PART ONE

Page 2: You Use Your Senses

CONCEPT: You observe using the senses of sight, hearing, touch, taste, and smell.

OBJECTIVE: I can tell about things I see, hear, smell, taste, and feel.

BIBLE REFERENCE: Proverbs 20:12.

PROCESS: observing

VOCABULARY: (senses, see, hear, smell, taste, feel, touch)

MATERIALS NEEDED: assorted objects to test senses (include shapes, colors, sounds, textures, odors, and flavors, as available or pictures of such objects), Worksheet 1, pencils

TEACHING PAGE 2:
Present the vocabulary. Match the vocabulary with objects or pictures. Ask which sense would be used to observe each. In most cases more than one sense will apply.

Call attention to the rebus pictures. Have them identified.

Ask for a volunteer to read the page aloud or have the class read it together.

Perhaps you might wish to read the text and have the children read the picture words as you go.

Provide time for questions and discussion of the text.

ACTIVITY:
Do Worksheet 1.

Read the direction or have a child read it.

Review the words in the box.

Let the children complete the page independently.

Check together and discuss.

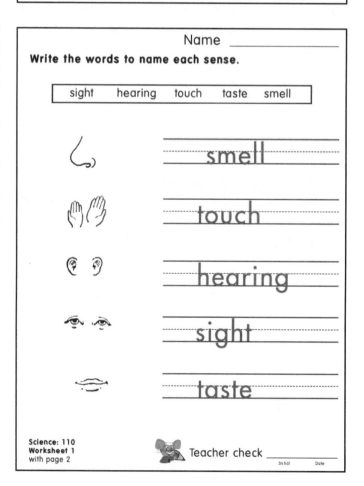

Page 3: Activity Page

MATERIALS NEEDED: pencils, crayons, LIFEPAC Tablet, popcorn

TEACHING PAGE 3:

Read the text to the class or have it read by a volunteer.

Ask a child to identify and read the direction sentence aloud.

Have the children complete the activity independently. They may color the picture.

Allow time for sharing and discussion of the completed pictures.

Encourage the children to describe how popcorn looks, sounds, tastes, smells, and feels.

ACTIVITIES:

1. Provide popcorn for the class. If possible make it in the classroom so that the children can experience the way all their senses can be used to observe the attributes of popcorn.

2. Have the children write this sentence in their LIFEPAC Tablet:

I use all my senses to observe the world around me.

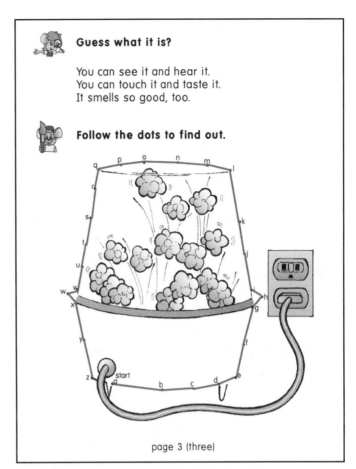

Guess what it is?

You can see it and hear it.
You can touch it and taste it.
It smells so good, too.

Follow the dots to find out.

page 3 (three)

Page 4 and 5: Sight

CONCEPT: You use your sense of sight to observe the world around you.

OBJECTIVE: I can tell about things I see, hear, smell, taste, and feel.

PROCESS: observing

READING INTEGRATION: recalling details, following directions

VOCABULARY: (shape, color, beautiful, weather, people, seasons, energy, winter, summer, pets, rain)

MATERIALS NEEDED: vocabulary word cards, pencils, Worksheets 2 and 3

TEACHING PAGES 4 and 5:

Review the vocabulary words using the word cards. As you present each word have the children try to recall what they have learned about each.

Example: Shape: Ask for volunteers to name the shapes they learned. Use the shapes from LIFEPAC 102 to review. Do similar activities with each vocabulary word.

Ask the children to identify all the shapes they can find in the illustrations on both pages.

Read the page aloud to the group, or have it read by a volunteer.

Ask for a volunteer to read the direction sentence on page 5.

Review the words in the word box.

Have the children complete the activity independently.

Check it together.

ACTIVITIES:

1. Do Worksheet 2 for practice and review of shapes.
Read the directions.
Let the children do the page independently.

YOU SEE

All around you are things to see.
You see the shapes of things.
You see the colors of things.
You see the beautiful world.
You see plants and animals.
You see people.
You see the weather.
You see the seasons.
You see energy at work.

page 4 (four)

Write the words that name the pictures of things you can see.

| winter | pets | energy |
| summer | people | rain |

rain   pets

energy   summer

winter   people

page 5 (five)

Check together. Give extra help to children who have forgotten shapes.

2. Do Worksheet 3 for a review of colors.

Read only the direction sentence.

Let the children read the sentences and do what each says independently.

Check together and give extra help to any child who still has difficulty with color words.

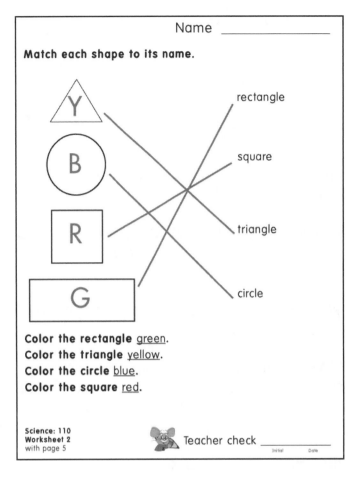

Name _____

Match each shape to its name.

rectangle

square

triangle

circle

Color the rectangle <u>green</u>.
Color the triangle <u>yellow</u>.
Color the circle <u>blue</u>.
Color the square <u>red</u>.

Science: 110
Worksheet 2
with page 5

Teacher check _____
Initial   Date

Name _____

Color the pictures to match the sentences.

The dog is brown.
The shirt is orange.
The sun is yellow.
The cat is black.
The tree is green.
The dress is purple.
The flag is red, white, and blue.

Science: 110
Worksheet 3
with page 5

Teacher check _____
Initial   Date

Pages 6 and 7: Hearing

CONCEPT: You use your ears to observe the world around you.

OBJECTIVE: I can tell about things I see, hear, smell, taste, and feel.

PROCESSES: observing, classifying, comparing, predicting

READING INTEGRATION: Main idea, recalling ideas, speaking in a group, following directions

VOCABULARY: (nature, machines, rhythm, tone, pitch, instruments, voice)

MATERIALS NEEDED: vocabulary word cards, pictures of things that make distinctive sounds as suggested by vocabulary words, Worksheets 4 and 5, pencils

TEACHING PAGES 6 and 7

Review the vocabulary words. As you present each word, have the children try to recall and demonstrate what they have learned about each.

Example: nature—have the children pick out from the pictures or name sounds they might hear in nature.

Read the text aloud to the class or have it read by volunteers.

Allow time for questions and discussion of sounds.

Discussion question: Encourage the children to think of times when sounds have been so loud or unpleasant that they are bothered by them (sound or noise pollution).

Ask a volunteer to read the direction sentence on page 7. Have the children complete the page independently. Check it together.

ACTIVITIES:

1. Do Worksheet 4.
   Read the directions.

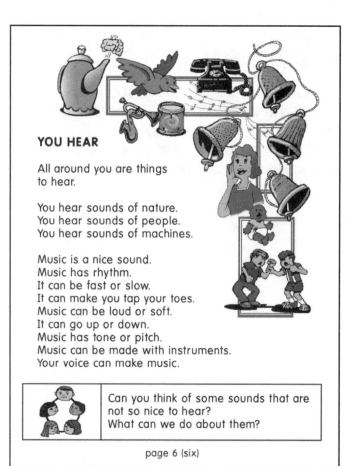

YOU HEAR

All around you are things to hear.

You hear sounds of nature.
You hear sounds of people.
You hear sounds of machines.

Music is a nice sound.
Music has rhythm.
It can be fast or slow.
It can make you tap your toes.
Music can be loud or soft.
It can go up or down.
Music has tone or pitch.
Music can be made with instruments.
Your voice can make music.

Can you think of some sounds that are not so nice to hear?
What can we do about them?

page 6 (six)

Circle all of the things you can hear.

page 7 (seven)

Let the children do the page independently.

Check together and discuss all sounds on the page including the nature sounds. Have the children color the picture.

2. Do Worksheet 5.

Read the direction. After the children circle the noisy things, discuss the entire illustration and the sentence at the bottom of the page.

Have the children color the picture.

Name _____

Circle sounds of nature. Color the pictures.

Science: 110
Worksheet 4
with page 7

Teacher check _____
Initial   Date

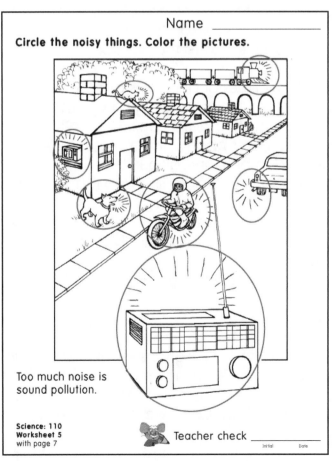

Name _____

Circle the noisy things. Color the pictures.

Too much noise is
sound pollution.

Science: 110
Worksheet 5
with page 7

Teacher check _____
Initial   Date

Pages 8 and 9: Taste and Smell

CONCEPT: You can observe by the senses of taste and smell.

OBJECTIVE: I can tell about things I see, hear, smell, taste, and feel.

PROCESSES: observing, comparing, classifying

READING INTEGRATION: main idea, recalling detail, speaking in a group, following directions

VOCABULARY: (pollution)

MATERIALS NEEDED: word card, pictures of things that create pollution you can smell, pencils, Worksheet 6

TEACHING PAGES 8 and 9:

Ask the children to recall what they learned about taste and smell and how they work together (see LIFEPAC 103).

Provide discussion time.

Read the text to the class or have it read by a volunteer.

Allow time for questions and discussion.

Discussion question: Show pictures of things that create pollution. Give the children an opportunity to present ideas of what can be done about it.

Ask a volunteer to find and read the two direction sentences on page 9.

Have the children complete the page independently, giving individual help as needed.

Check together.

ACTIVITY:

Do Worksheet 6.

Read the directions. Make sure the children understand the directions. Let them do the page independently. Check together. Clear up any difficulties.

YOU TASTE AND SMELL

You can observe
with your mouth and
your nose.
When you wake up
in the morning,
you smell and taste the good food
that gives you energy
for the day.

Your nose can smell
good things.
It can smell flowers.
Your nose can smell
bad things.
Some things make
the air smell bad.
They are called pollution.

Can you do anything
about pollution?

page 8 (eight)

Circle good foods for breakfast.

Circle the answer.

I can smell a _____ .
flower / rock

I can taste a _____ .
dress / pie

I can hear _____ .
music / block

page 9 (nine)

Name _____

Which sense do you use?

Write I **for taste.**

Write S **for smell.**

Write TS **if you can taste and smell.**

S

TS

TS

T

Science 110
Worksheet 6
with page 9

Teacher check _____

Initial   Date

Pages 10 and 11: Touch

CONCEPT: You can use your sense of touch to learn about the world around you.

OBJECTIVE: I can tell about things I see, hear, smell, taste, and feel.

PROCESSES: observing, comparing, classifying

READING INTEGRATION: main idea, rhyming, speaking in a group, recalling details, following directions

VOCABULARY: (touch)

MATERIALS NEEDED: items with different textures and consistencies for the children to feel and compare, pencils, Worksheet 7

TEACHING PAGES 10 and 11:
Read the paragraph to the class or have it read by a volunteer.

Discuss the pictures. Have the children supply words that tell how each picture might feel.
Examples: The pillow is soft or fluffy.
Water is wet.

Read the poem aloud. Ask the children to listen for rhyming words and words that tell how things feel.

Reread the poem with the children reading aloud with you.

Provide some time for the children to tell about some "inside" feelings. *Examples:* happy, sad

Ask a volunteer to read the direction sentence on page 11.

Have the children complete the activity independently.

Check it together.

ACTIVITY:
Do Worksheet 7.

All necessary directions are on the Worksheet.

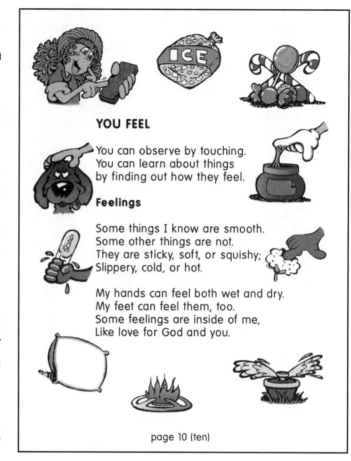

YOU FEEL

You can observe by touching. You can learn about things by finding out how they feel.

Feelings

Some things I know are smooth.
Some other things are not.
They are sticky, soft, or squishy;
Slippery, cold, or hot.

My hands can feel both wet and dry.
My feet can feel them, too.
Some feelings are inside of me,
Like love for God and you.

page 10 (ten)

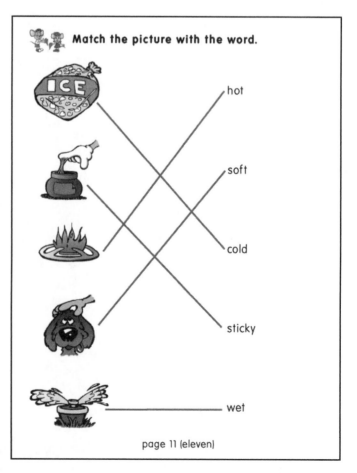

Match the picture with the word.

hot

soft

cold

sticky

wet

page 11 (eleven)

Name _____

Make a FEELY BOX.

You need:	
shoebox	tape
scissors	some things to feel

What to do.

1. Cut a hole in one end of the box.

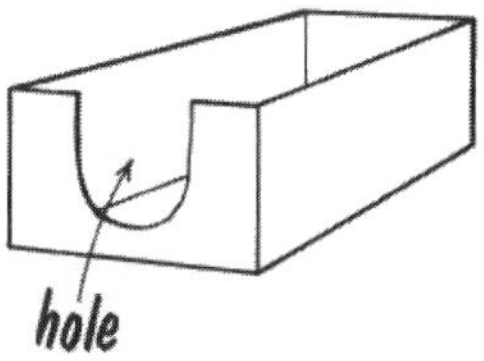

hole

2. Tape the cover on the box.

3. Put something in the box. Ask a friend to guess what it is by feeling.

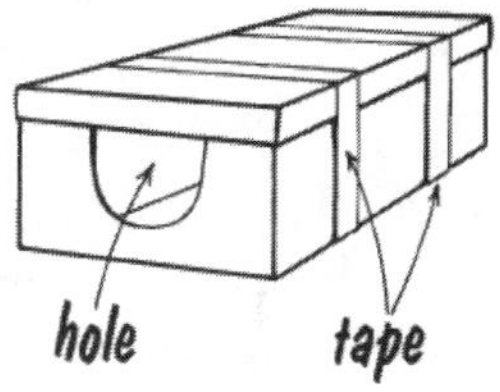

hole   *tape*

Science: 110
Worksheet 7
with page 11

Teacher check _____
Initial   Date

297

Pages 12 and 13: Self Test 1

CONCEPT: evaluation

OBJECTIVE: I can tell about things I see, hear, smell, taste, and touch.

READING INTEGRATION: following directions, recalling details

VOCABULARY: Review all the vocabulary.

MATERIALS NEEDED: pencils

TEACHING PAGES 12 and 13:

Review the vocabulary words.

Read all the directions with the children. Be sure the directions are understood.

The general proficiency of your group should dictate whether you choose to direct the self test or allow the children to proceed independently once directions are given.

In either case you should be available to answer questions and to help with the vocabulary as needed.

Check immediately. Review concepts missed individually or in groups.

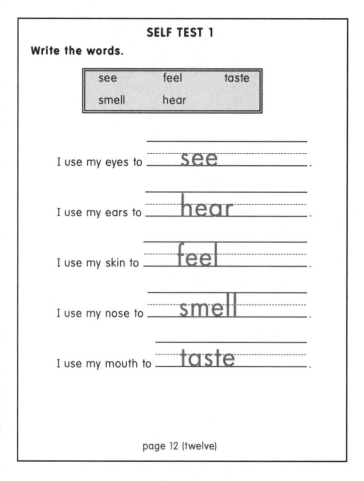

II. PART TWO

Pages 14 and 15: You Use Your Mind

CONCEPT: God gave you a mind to learn and think.

OBJECTIVES:
I can show how things I observe are alike and different.
I can tell how things I observe will grow or change.

PROCESSES: observing, comparing, classifying, predicting

READING INTEGRATION: main idea, recalling detail, following directions,

VOCABULARY: (mind, think, learn, alike, different, work, change)

MATERIALS NEEDED: vocabulary word cards; pictures of living things (plants, animals); non-living things (machines, tools, land forms, seasons, weather), LIFEPAC Tablet, pencils, crayons

TEACHING PAGES 14 and 15:
Present the vocabulary. Discuss the meaning of each word:
mind: the part of you that thinks, feels, and wills.
think: to have ideas. Learn: to find out, come to know.
alike: in the same way.
different: not the same. work: to act, operate.
change: to become different.
Read the text aloud to the group or have it read by a volunteer.
Have the children use the pictures to group things that are alike, to identify differences, and to tell about things that work, grow, and change.
Ask a volunteer to read the direction sentence on page 15.

II. YOU USE YOUR MIND

God gave you a mind.
Your mind helps you think.
Your mind helps you learn.
You can learn
how things are alike.
You can learn
how things are different.
You can learn
how things work.
You can learn
how things change.

page 14 (fourteen)

Draw a picture of something you like to think about.

page 15 (fifteen)

Have the children complete the page independently.

Allow plenty of time for all the children to tell about their pictures.

ACTIVITY:

Have the children write this thankful prayer in their tablets:

I like to think.

I like to learn.

Thank you, God, for giving me a mind to do both.

Page 16: Alike and Different

CONCEPT: Your mind and your senses help you learn that things are alike and different.

OBJECTIVE: I can show how things I observe are alike and different.

PROCESSES: observing, classifying, comparing

READING INTEGRATION: main idea, speaking in a group

MATERIALS NEEDED: set of objects, shapes or pictures to classify into groups, Worksheet 8

TEACHING PAGE 16:

Read the text aloud to the class or have it read by volunteers.

Practice grouping (classifying) beginning with the pictures on the page (see discussion question).

Example: All the pictures on the page are of animals. Group them as wild, farm, and pet animals.

ACTIVITY:

Do Worksheet 8.

Read the directions. Make sure the children know what each picture is.

Let the children do the page independently.

Check the page by having the children read and spell each item they have written for each list. Discuss other ways of grouping the living things.

THINGS ALIKE AND DIFFERENT

Some things look the same.
Some things belong
to the same group.
These things are alike.

Some things are not the same.
Some things do not belong
to the same group.
These things are different.

Look at the pictures.
How are these pictures alike?
How are they different?

page 16 (sixteen)

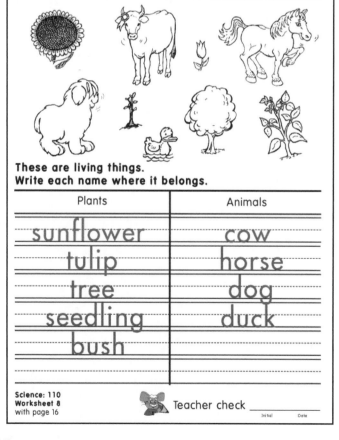

Name _____

These are living things.
Write each name where it belongs.

Plants	Animals
sunflower	cow
tulip	horse
tree	dog
seedling	duck
bush	

Science: 110
Worksheet 8
with page 16

Teacher check _____
Initial   Date

Page 17: Activity Page

MATERIALS NEEDED: banner paper, old magazines, scissors, glue, pencils

TEACHING PAGE 17:

Discussion question: Read the questions aloud. Have the children tell how the pictures are alike (they are all foods) and different (some are fruits, some are vegetables, and some are meats).

Ask a volunteer to find and read the direction sentence.

Have the children complete the page independently.

Check it together.

ACTIVITY:

Divide your class into five groups. Give each group some old magazines, scissors, glue, and a large piece of butcher paper. Assign a food group to each group of children.

Include *Dairy, Meats, Vegetable, Fruits,* and *Grain Products* (breads and cereals).

Have them make collages of the pictures they find.

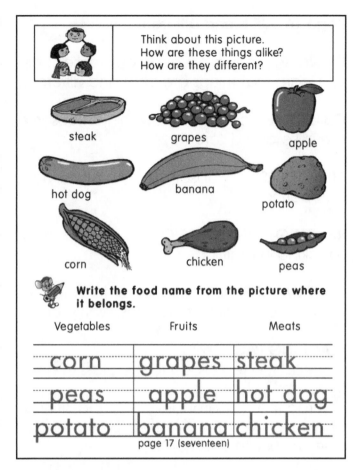

Think about this picture.
How are these things alike?
How are they different?

steak   grapes   apple

hot dog   banana   potato

corn   chicken   peas

Write the food name from the picture where it belongs.

Vegetables	Fruits	Meats
corn	grapes	steak
peas	apple	hot dog
potato	banana	chicken

page 17 (seventeen)

Pages 18 and 19: Things That Work

CONCEPTS:
Your mind can help you find ways to make work easier.

Men have invented machines to do many jobs.

Some of these machines are very simple.

OBJECTIVE: I can tell how things I observe are alike and different.

PROCESSES: observing, comparing, classifying

READING INTEGRATION: main idea, recalling detail, speaking in a group, following details

VOCABULARY: lever, wheel, inclined plane, simple machine

MATERIALS NEEDED: vocabulary word cards; pictures of various levers, wheels, and inclined planes from LIFEPAC 109; Worksheet 9; pencils; crayons

TEACHING PAGES 18 and 19:
Briefly review the vocabulary, matching it with the pictures.

Read the sentences and picture captions to the children or have them read by volunteers.

Ask: "How are the things in the pictures alike?" (They are all simple machines.)

"How are they different?" (The children should be able to describe the different attributes and functions of the simple machines.)

Ask a volunteer to find and read the three direction sentences on page 19.

Have the children complete the page independently.

Check it together.

Discussion question: Have the children describe the job each simple machine can do.

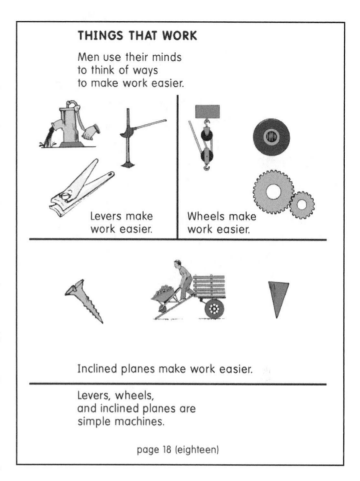

THINGS THAT WORK

Men use their minds to think of ways to make work easier.

Levers make work easier.

Wheels make work easier.

Inclined planes make work easier.

Levers, wheels, and inclined planes are simple machines.

page 18 (eighteen)

Circle the levers.

Circle the wheels.

Circle the inclined planes.

Can you tell what these simple machines can do?

page 19 (nineteen)

ACTIVITY:

Do Worksheet 9.

Encourage the children to use their imaginations for this Worksheet. Read the directions to the children and let them complete the sheet independently.

Help them with spelling if they need help.

Have the children write one or two paragraphs about their machine in their Tablet.

Allow sufficient time for each child to explain his machine and what it does and to read his paragraphs.

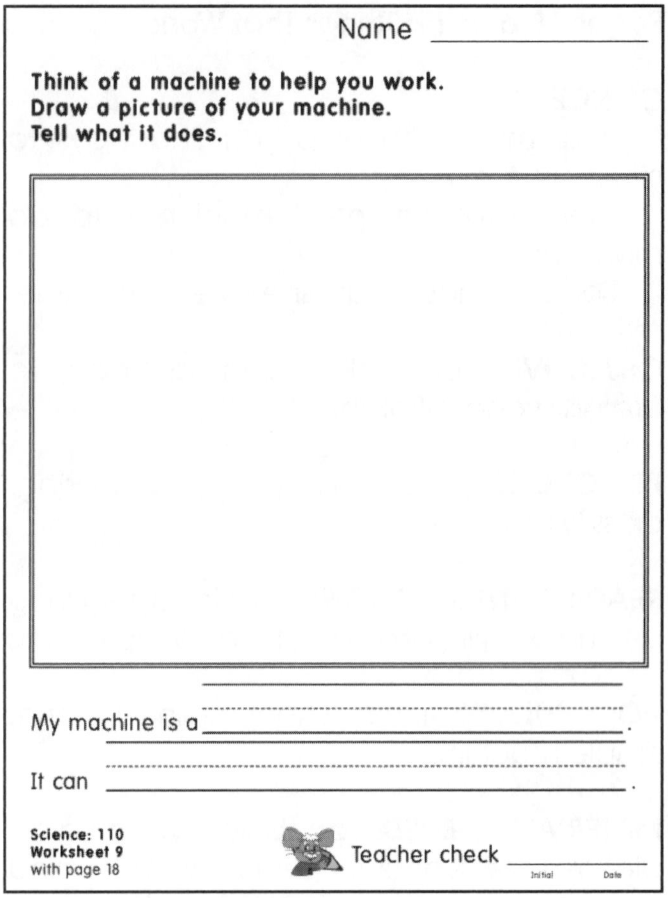

Name _____

Think of a machine to help you work.
Draw a picture of your machine.
Tell what it does.

My machine is a _____.

It can _____.

Science: 110
Worksheet 9
with page 18

Teacher check _____
Initial   Date

Page 20: Things that Change

CONCEPT: Our minds help us to learn about things that grow and change.

OBJECTIVE: I can tell how things I observe will grow or change.

PROCESS: observing

READING INTEGRATION: main idea, recalling detail

VOCABULARY: (change, grow, weather, seasons, energy)

MATERIALS: vocabulary word cards, pictures of things that grow or change in some other way

TEACHING PAGE 20:

Review the vocabulary. Display the pictures and have the children match a word with the picture.

Examples: A snow picture — change or weather.

A lamb — change, grow.

Read the text aloud or have it read by a student.

Provide time for questions and discussion.

Tell the children that the next few pages will help them remember how things grow and change.

THINGS THAT CHANGE

Many things change.
Some things get bigger.
They grow.
Some things change in other ways.
Weather changes.
Seasons change.
Energy helps things to change,
grow, and move.
Most energy comes from the sun.

page 20 (twenty)

Page 21: Activity Page

MATERIALS NEEDED: pencils, Worksheet 10, waxed paper, colored tissue paper, yarn, iron, newspaper

TEACHING PAGE 21:

Ask a student to find and read the two direction sentences.

When the directions are understood, have the children complete the page independently. Give individual help as needed.

Check it together.

ACTIVITIES:

1.   Do Worksheet 10.

Read and discuss each stage.

Supply more pictures from books if they are available.

Have the children color the picture.

2.   Make butterflies to decorate your classroom. Here are directions for one kind. Wax paper butterflies: Provide each child with 2 sheets of waxed paper, scraps of colored tissue, and yarn. You will need newspaper and an iron.

Have the children place the tissue scraps between the two pieces of waxed paper.

You then place the child's preparation between two sheets of newspaper. Iron the paper until the tissue is adhered firmly to the waxed paper. When cool, remove the newspaper.

Have the children glue yarn on the waxed paper in the shape of a butterfly. Have them trim the excess waxed paper away. Finished products are very effective against a window or hanging as a mobile where light can flow through them.

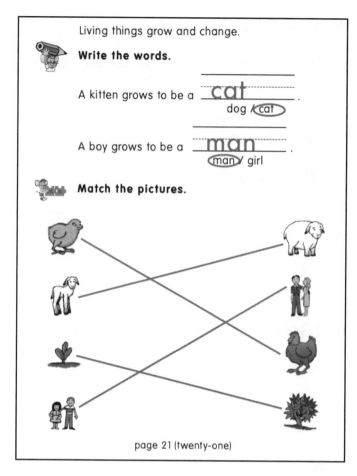

Living things grow and change.

Write the words.

A kitten grows to be a ___cat___ .
dog /cat

A boy grows to be a ___man___ .
man / girl

Match the pictures.

page 21 (twenty-one)

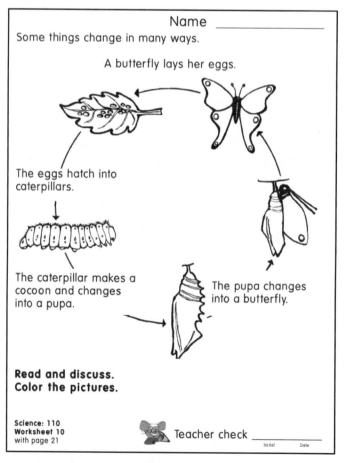

Name _____

Some things change in many ways.

A butterfly lays her eggs.

The eggs hatch into caterpillars.

The caterpillar makes a cocoon and changes into a pupa.

The pupa changes into a butterfly.

Read and discuss.
Color the pictures.

Science: 110
Worksheet 10
with page 21

Teacher check _____
Initial   Date

Page 22: Activity Page

MATERIALS NEEDED: pictures of different kinds of weather to discuss and compare, pencils, crayons, Worksheet 11

TEACHING PAGE 22:

Display the weather pictures. Ask the children to think about and tell which weather changes occur as the seasons change and which weather changes might occur in one day.

Ask a volunteer to read the statement and the direction sentence.

Have the children complete the activity independently.

Allow time for the children to share their pictures (they should depict rain).

Discussion question: Give the children an opportunity to share their experiences with the weather.

ACTIVITY:

Do Worksheet 11.

Read the direction. Tell the children to draw their pictures and to write stories about their pictures that tell why the weather shown is their favorite kind, what they like to do in this kind of weather, and what changes they see in this kind of weather.

Allow time for the reading of each story as each child shows his picture.

page 22 (twenty-two)

Page 23: Activity Page

MATERIALS NEEDED: pictures from page 22, LIFEPAC Tablet, pencils

TEACHING PAGE 23:

Display the pictures. Have the children group them according to season: spring, summer, fall, and winter.

Ask a volunteer to find and read the direction sentences.

Review the names of the seasons.

Have the children complete the activity independently.

Check it together and discuss the illustrations.

ACTIVITY:

Have the children write this poem in their LIFEPAC Tablets:

Summer is hot
Winter is not
Fall and spring
Are in-between.
        Phyllis A. MacDonald

Name the seasons. Put the words under the pictures.

| spring | summer | autumn | winter |

autumn   winter

summer   spring

page 23 (twenty-three)

Pages 24 and 25: Self Test 2

CONCEPT: evaluation

OBJECTIVE:

I can tell things I see, hear, smell, taste, and feel.

I can show how things I observe are alike and different.

I can tell how things I observe will grow and change.

READING INTEGRATION: following directions, recalling details

VOCABULARY: Review all the vocabulary.

MATERIALS NEEDED: pencils

TEACHING PAGES 24 and 25:

Review the vocabulary and concepts for sections.

Read all the directions with the children. Be sure they are understood.

The general proficiency of your group will dictate whether you choose to direct the self test or allow the children to proceed independently once directions are given.

In either case you should be available to answer questions and to help with vocabulary, as needed.

Check immediately and go over the test with each child. Review any concepts missed.

Have children who still have difficulty review the individual LIFEPACs as well as the sections from LIFEPAC 110. An aide or parent should supervise this review.

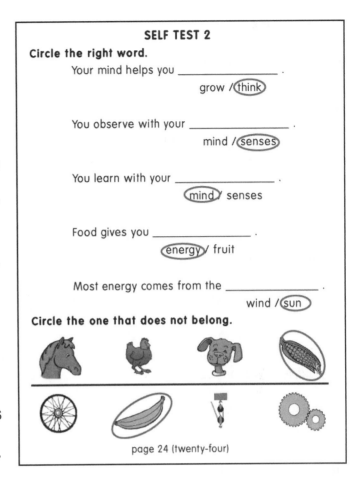

page 24 (twenty-four)

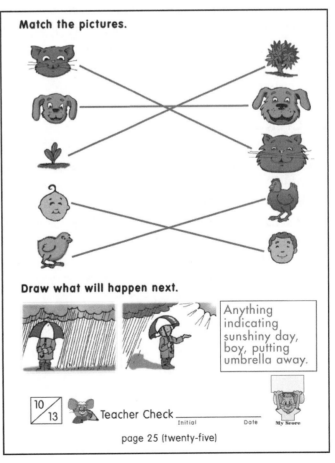

page 25 (twenty-five)

III. PART THREE

Page 26: You Use Your Love

CONCEPTS:
Everyone can help take care of himself and the world in which he lives.

If each person loves and cares for his neighbor, the world will be a better place to live.

OBJECTIVE: I can tell ways my love will make the world better.

PROCESSES: observing, comparing, predicting

READING INTEGRATION: main idea, speaking in a group

VOCABULARY: (healthy)

MATERIALS NEEDED: pictures of people doing things that show their love for themselves, for each other, and for the world around them (include things like sharing, doing tasks, helping others, good health habits, picking up litter, saving energy, and so on).

TEACHING PAGE 26:
Display and discuss the pictures. Ask the children if they can tell what all the pictures have in common (they depict people taking care of themselves and their world).

Read the page aloud to the class or have it read by volunteers.

Ask the children to think of and tell about ways they can take care of themselves and their world.

III. YOU USE YOUR LOVE

God loves you.
He wants you to love, too.
You can love yourself.
You can love the world
you live in.

YOU LOVE YOURSELF

To love is to take care.
A mother takes care of a baby.
You take care of your pet.

You can take care
of yourself, too.
If you take care of yourself,
you will stay healthy.

page 26 (twenty-six)

Page 27: Activity Page

VOCABULARY: (sleep, eat, exercise, clean)

MATERIALS NEEDED: crayons, pencils, Worksheet 12

TEACHING PAGE 27:

Ask a volunteer to find and read the direction sentences.

Review the vocabulary words.

Have the children complete the page independently.

Check it together, giving the children time to show and tell about their pictures.

ACTIVITY:

Do Worksheet 12.

Read the direction. Have the children read the word/phrase side of the page.

Let them do the matching.

Check together and ask the children:

"What kinds of exercises do you do?"

"What kinds of food are good for you?"

"How many hours of sleep do you need?"

"How do you keep yourself clean?"

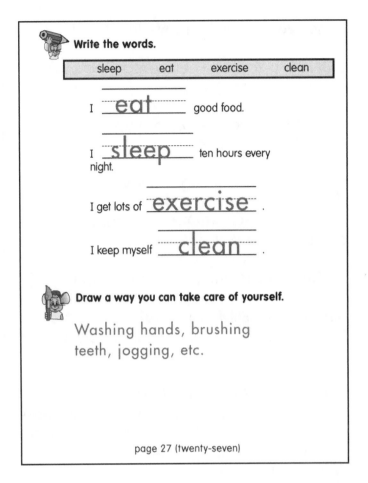

Write the words.

sleep	eat	exercise	clean

I ___eat___ good food.

I ___sleep___ ten hours every night.

I get lots of ___exercise___.

I keep myself ___clean___.

Draw a way you can take care of yourself.

Washing hands, brushing teeth, jogging, etc.

page 27 (twenty-seven)

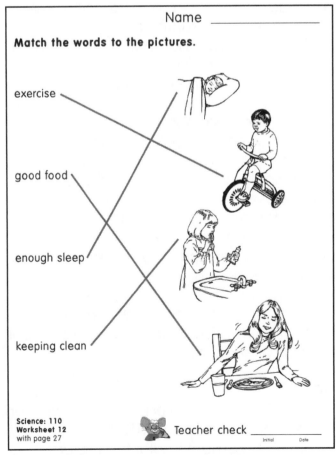

Name _____

Match the words to the pictures.

exercise

good food

enough sleep

keeping clean

Science: 110
Worksheet 12
with page 27

Teacher check _____
Initial   Date

Pages 28 and 29: You Love the World

CONCEPT: You can help keep God's world clean and beautiful.

OBJECTIVE: I can tell ways my love will make the world better.

PROCESSES: observing, classifying

READING INTEGRATION: main idea, recalling detail, following directions

VOCABULARY: (litter, tools, trash, toys)

MATERIALS NEEDED: LIFEPAC Tablet, picture from page 26, Worksheet 13, pencils, paper sack, string, crayons

TEACHING PAGES 28 and 29:

Display the pictures. Have the children group them under these headings: Caring for Yourself, Caring for Others, Caring for the World Around You.

Read the page aloud to the class or have it read by volunteers.

Discuss things children can do at school, at home, or in other places to help keep God's world clean and beautiful.

Ask a volunteer to read the direction sentences on page 29.

Review the vocabulary words.

Distribute materials.

Carefully go over the directions for the litter bags.

Demonstrate how it is made.

Have the children complete the activities independently. Give individual help as needed.

Check the first activity together.

Allow the children to share their litter bags. They may be hung on desks for school litter or taken home.

ACTIVITY:

Do Worksheet 13. Read the sentence or have it read. Discuss the illustration.

Have the children color the picture.

page 28 (twenty-eight)

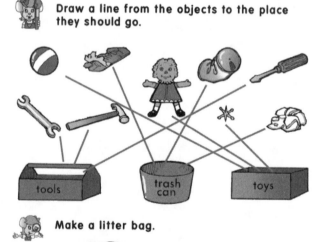

Draw a line from the objects to the place they should go.

tools   trash can   toys

  Make a litter bag.

You need:
a paper bag
crayons
string

1. Write <u>LITTER</u> on your bag.
2. Draw some pictures on it.
3. Fold the top down.
4. Ask your teacher to help you put the string on the bag.
5. Decide where to put your litter bag.

page 29 (twenty-nine)

Have them write two paragraphs in their Tablets telling what they can do to help make the world more beautiful.

Name _____

These children are making a pretty garden.

Color the picture.

Science: 110
Worksheet 13
with page 29

Teacher check _____
Initial   Date

Page 30: Saving Energy

CONCEPT: You can take care of the world by saving energy.

OBJECTIVE: I can tell ways my love will make the world better.

PROCESS: observing

READING INTEGRATION: main idea, recalling detail, speaking in a group

VOCABULARY: (energy, save, waste, refrigerator)

MATERIALS: pictures of energy producers and energy users from LIFEPAC 108, Worksheets 14 and 15, pencils, crayons

TEACHING PAGE 30:

Using the pictures, review the concepts from Science 108. Have the children recall how energy is produced, how it is used, and how it can be saved.

Read the page to the class or have it read by volunteers.

Ask the children to relate the text to the pictures. Ask how the pictures could be changed to show that energy is being saved.

Example: The light switch could be off.

Discussion question: Give the children an opportunity to recall and tell about other ways they and their families can save energy.

ACTIVITIES:

1. Do Worksheet 14.
    Read the directions.
    When the children complete the picture, ask questions such as these: "How does this bike save energy"
    "What simple machines do you see in the picture?"
2. Do Worksheet 15.
    Read the directions. Discuss possible responses. Help with spelling.
    Allow time for each child to read his sentences.

You can help take care
of the world by saving energy.
Sometimes you waste energy.
You forget to turn off lights.
You ride in a car
when you could walk.
You leave the refrigerator
door open.
Being careful not
to waste energy
will help everyone.

 Tell some ways you can help save energy.

page 30 (thirty)

Name _____

Follow the dots to see what saves energy. Start with A. Color your picture.

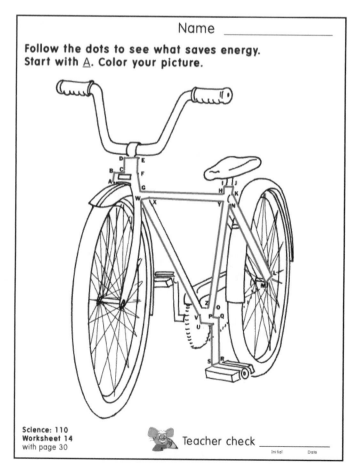

Science: 110
Worksheet 14
with page 30

Teacher check _____
Initial   Date

Name _____

Write ways that you can help save energy.
Ask your teacher to help.

Ride bike, walk, close
refrigerator door, turn
off lights, etc.

Science: 110
Worksheet 15
with page 30

Teacher check _____
Initial   Date

Page 31: Activity Page

MATERIALS NEEDED: pencils

TEACHING PAGE 31:

Ask a volunteer to read the direction sentence.

Have the children complete the page independently, giving individual help as needed.

Check it together.

Have the children tell about or demonstrate the exercises the boy is doing (jumping jacks, pushups, toe touches, sit-ups).

The class may enjoy an exercise session using the exercises pictured.

Circle the right word.

I can save_____by riding a bike.
(energy)/ litter

Something you throw on the ground is _____.
(litter)/ toy

Exercise and sleep help make you _____.
(healthy)/ energy

Good food gives you_____.
healthy /(energy)

To love is to_____.
waste /(take care)

page 31 (thirty-one)

Pages 32 and 33: Self Test 3

CONCEPT: evaluation

OBJECTIVES:

I can tell about things I see, hear, smell, taste, and feel.

I can show how things I observe are alike and different.

I can tell how things I observe will grow or change.

I can tell ways my love will make the world better.

READING INTEGRATION: following directions, recalling details

VOCABULARY: Review all the vocabulary.

MATERIALS NEEDED: pencils, Worksheet 16, crayons, large drawing paper

TEACHING PAGES 32 and 33:

Review the vocabulary and concepts for the entire LIFEPAC, with special emphasis on section 3.

Read through the directions for the self test with the group. Answer any questions the children might have.

The general proficiency of your group will dictate whether you choose to direct the self test or allow the children to proceed independently once directions are given.

In either case, you should be available to answer questions and to help with vocabulary, as needed.

Check immediately. Review any concepts missed.

For those children who need extra help, have them work with a classroom helper or a parent to prepare for the LIFEPAC Test.

ACTIVITY:

Do Worksheet 16.

All necessary directions are on the Worksheet.

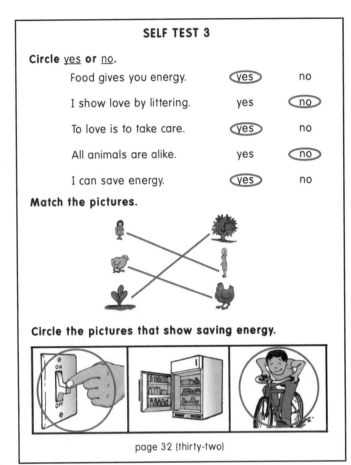

page 32 (thirty-two)

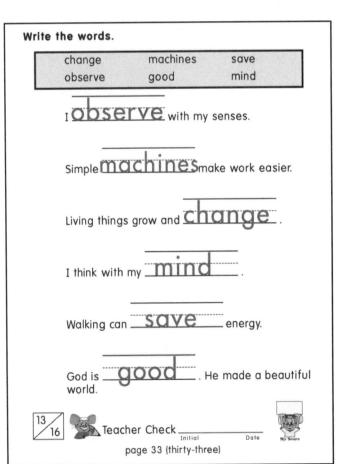

page 33 (thirty-three)

Name _____

Make a change collage.

1. **Color the picture.**
2. **Cut it out.**
2. **Paste it on a big sheet of paper.**
3. **Cut out or draw pictures of other changes you have studied.**

Science: 110
Worksheet 16
with page 33

Teacher check _____

Initial   Date

LIFEPAC TEST AND ALTERNATE LIFEPAC TEST:

Administer the test to the class as a group. Ask to have directions read or read them to the class. In either case, be sure that the children clearly understand. Put examples on the board if it seems necessary. Give ample time for each activity to be completed before going on to the next.

Correct immediately and discuss with the child.

Review any concepts that have been missed.

Give those children who do not achieve the 80% score additional copies of the worksheets and a list of vocabulary words to study. A parent or a classroom helper should help in the review.

When the child is ready, give the Alternate LIFEPAC Test. Use the same procedure as for the LIFEPAC TEST.

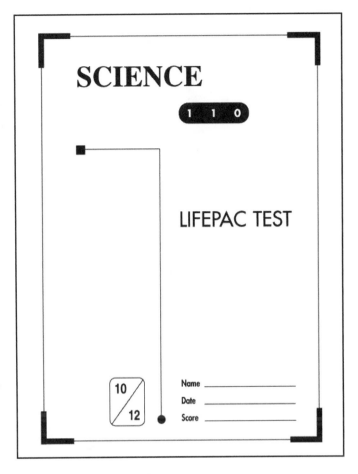

SCIENCE

1 1 0

LIFEPAC TEST

10/12

Name _____

Date _____

Score _____

SCIENCE 110: LIFEPAC TEST

Circle the right answer.

Food gives you _____ to move and grow.
(energy) / change

To take care is to _____ .
(love) / waste

I use my _____ to observe.
mind / (senses)

Walking can _____ energy.
(save) / waste

Draw a line to match.

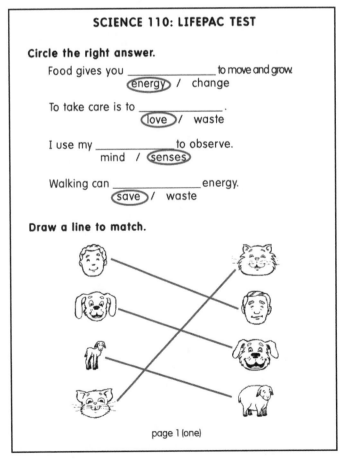

page 1 (one)

223

Circle the one that is different.

Draw what will happen next.

young man

page 2 (two)

NOTES

page 3 (three)

SCIENCE

1 1 0

ALTERNATE
LIFEPAC TEST

12/14

Name _____

Date _____

Score _____

SCIENCE 110: ALTERNATE LIFEPAC TEST

Draw a line to match.

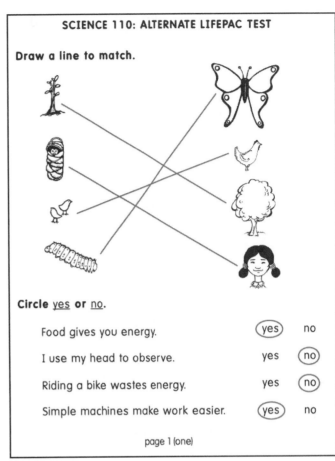

Circle <u>yes</u> **or** <u>no</u>.

Food gives you energy.	(yes)	no
I use my head to observe.	yes	(no)
Riding a bike wastes energy.	yes	(no)
Simple machines make work easier.	(yes)	no

page 1 (one)

Circle the one that is different.

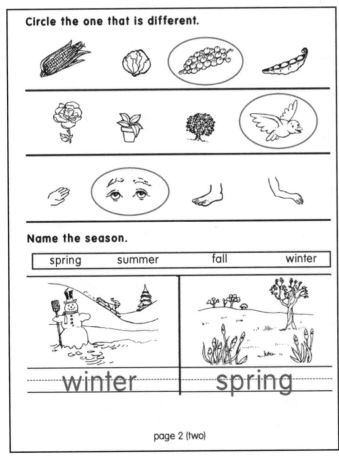

Name the season.

spring	summer	fall	winter

winter   spring

page 2 (two)

Draw what will happen next.

Any scene showing winter:
bare trees; snow; etc.

page 3 (three)

SCIENCE 101–110: CUMULATIVE WORD LIST

act	cereal	drink	gear(s)
air	change	drive	gills
almost	changes	driving	giraffe
angry	check	drop	glass
animal	cheese	dry	goat
answer	chick	eagle	goldfish
anything	chicken	eaglet	good
apple	chop	ears	grain
atom	church	earth	grass
autumn	circle	easier	grassland
ax	cities	easily	green
back	clean	easy	grew
banana	climate	eat	group
bear	clippers	eggs	grown-up
beat	clock	electricity	guard
belong	cloud	elephants	hamster
berries	coal	energy	hands
better	coconut	engines	happy
big	cold	exercise	harm
bigger	color	eye	hay
bird	community	eyes	healthy
bitter	cone	fact	hear
black	cooler	fantasy	heaven
blue	cook	farm	heavy
board	corn	farmer	hedge
body	cover	feather	help
bowl	cow	feeling	herd
brain	creature	feet	high
bread	cub	fern	hippopotamus
breakfast	damp	first	hole
breathe	dark	fish	home
brown	date	fisherman	honey
buds	deer	fit	horse
buffalo	den	flag	hot
build	desert	flower	hours
burn	dew	fluffy	house
bushes	different	force	house plant
cactus	dinner	food	hunter
cacti	dog	forest	important
cage	dolphin	forth	inclined plane
calf	donkey	fruit	invisible
cannot	doorstop	fuel	ivy
car	dot	fulcrum	jump
cat	dove	garden	jumping
catch	down	gasoline	kitchen

kitten
knife
lake
land
leaf
leaves
lemons
lemonade
lever
lift
lilypad
lion
light
living
lizard
load
long
loud
louder
low
machine
magnifying glass
make-believe
mane
maple
march
Mary
match
meadow
meat
massage
metal
microscope
middle
milk
morning
mouse
mountain
move
moving
munch
mushroom
muscles
mysterious
mail
narrow
nature

nerves
nest
nestling
Noah
noise
nose
nuclear
nutcracker
oak
oar
oarlock
ocean
o'clock
oil
open
orange
outer
outside
owner
pain
pair
parakeet
peanut butter
peas
pencil
pick
picnic
picture
pig
pine
pink
pitch
place
plains
plant
playing
pliers
plow
prairie
praise
pulley(s)
purple
push
push-up
raccoon
rain
rainbow

raindrop
ramp
read
rectangle
red
replace
rest
rhythm
ring
river
roadrunner
rock
root
rope(s)
rough
run
sad
safe
sailing ships
salty
same
sand
sandwich
school
scientist
scissors
seaweed
seashore
season
screw
screwdriver
see
seed
shape(s)
sharp
sheep
side
simple machine
sing
singing
sit-up
size(s)
skin
skip
sleep
slippery
small

smaller
smell
smooth
snack
snake
snow
soft
soil
solar
solid
sour
sound
sparrow
spinach
spring
square
squash
stalk
starfish
stayed
steam
sticky
still
stone(s)
strong
stronger
struck
sugar
summer
sunlight
sunshine
supper
sweet
sweet potato
tail
taller
taste
teeth
themselves
thick
thin
through
thunder
tight
toe-touch
tomato
tone

tool
toolbox
touch
teach
trains
travel
tree
triangle
trucks
true
trunk
turn
turtle
useful
valley
vegetables
vibrate
vibration
vines
voice
wagon
walk
warmer
waste
watch
water
waves
weather
wedge
wet
wheat
wheel(s)
wheelchair
white
wide
wildflower
wind
windmill
winter
wood(s)
woodland
work
write
yard
yellow

LIFEPAC

WORKSHEETS

Reproducible Worksheets
for use with the Science 100
Teacher's Guide

Name _____

Cut out the sentence endings.
Glue them in the right places.

Glue endings here.

A chick will grow to be

A seed will grow to be

A puppy will grow to be

A cub will grow to be

A fawn will grow to be

- -

| a deer. | a bear. |

| a plant. | a chicken. |

| a dog. |

Teacher check _____

Initial   Date

Show the way the baby should grow.

Name _____

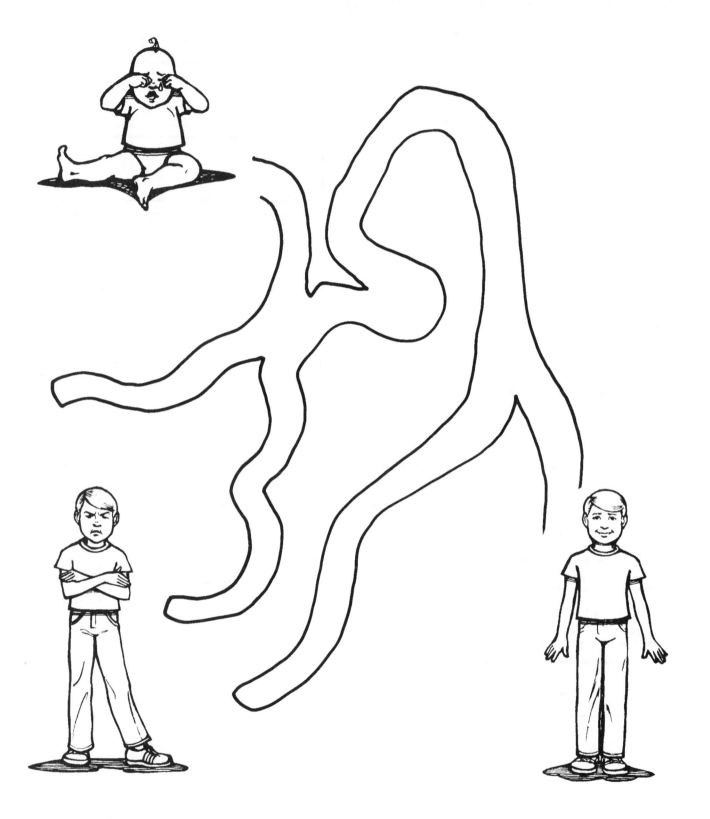

Science 106
Worksheet 2
with page 8

Teacher check _____

Initial   Date

232

Name _____

Draw a 😊 **thing you can do.**

Science 106
Worksheet 3
with page 10

Teacher check _____
Initial   Date

233

Name _____

Here is a baby animal.
See what it will grow up to be.

tadpole

Follow the dots.
Color the pictures.

Science 106
Worksheet 4
with page 13

Teacher check _____

Initial   Date

234

Here is another baby animal.
See what it will grow up to be.

fuzzy caterpillar

Follow the dots.
Color the pictures.

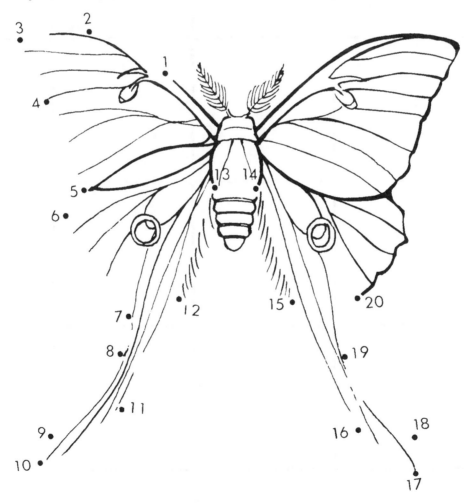

Science 106
Worksheet 5
with page 13

Teacher check _____

Initial   Date

235

Name _____

Foods I Eat

	Breakfast	Lunch	Dinner	Snacks
Day 1				
Day 2				
Day 3				
Day 4				
Day 5				

Science 106
Worksheet 6
with page 14

Teacher check _____
Initial   Date

236

Name _____

Super Peanut Butter

1 pound salt peanuts without shells
1/4 cup wheat germ
1/4 cup honey

Grind the peanuts.
Add the wheat germ and honey.
Stir until smooth.
Serve on celery sticks.

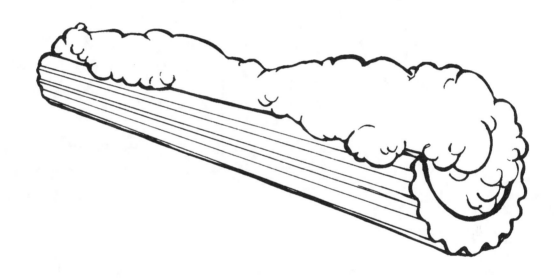

Color the celery <u>green</u>.
Color the peanut butter <u>brown</u>.

- -

Memory verse:

    Know ye not that ye are the temple of God, and that the Spirit of God dwelleth in you? I Corinthians 3:16

Science 106
Worksheet 7
with page 16

 Teacher check _____
                                                Initial   Date

Color the picture.

Name _____

Science 106
Worksheet 8
with page 16

Teacher check _____

Initial   Date

238

Draw the hands on the clock to show the time you eat dinner.

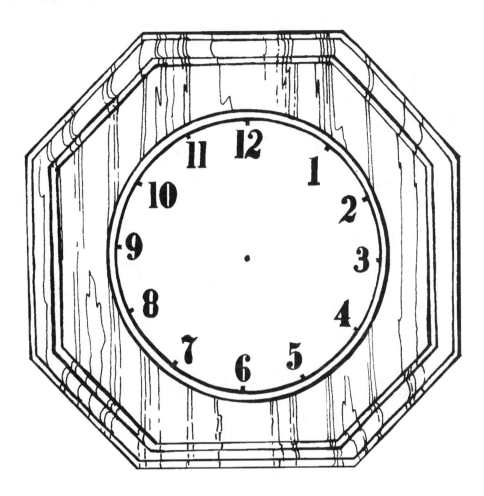

Finish the sentence.

_____

I eat dinner at _____ o'clock.

Science 106
Worksheet 9
with page 18

Teacher check _____
Initial   Date

239

Color the puzzle.

Name _____

Color

r-red
t-black
d-green
s-blue

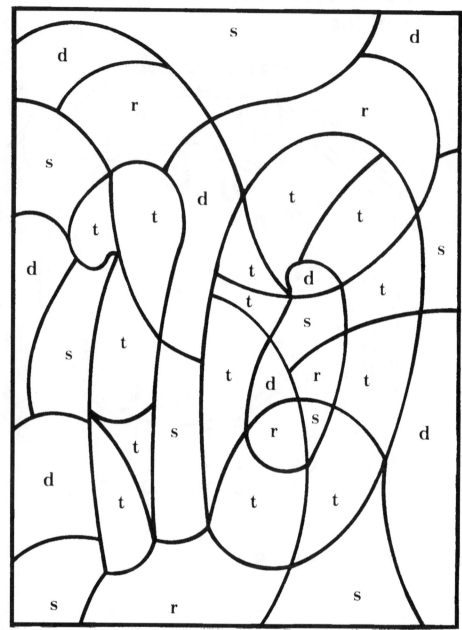

Circle the answer.

How many hours should you sleep?

2   5   8   10

Teacher check _____

Initial   Date

Name _____

Circle the answer.

Plants, animals, and people can _____.

grow / sleep

A grown-up needs _____ hours of sleep.

many / eight

Soda pop _____ good for you.

is / is not

Milk _____ good for you.

is / is not

A fawn will grow to be a _____.

bear / deer

Science 106
Worksheet 11
with page 23

 Teacher check _____

Initial   Date

241

Write the words.

exercise	healthy	playing

_____

_____ is good exercise.

_____

_____ helps you grow strong.

Food, sleep and exercise help you grow up

_____

_____ .

Color Dan playing.

Teacher check _____

Initial   Date

Name _____

Follow the dots to see what you use to <u>jump</u>, <u>run</u>, <u>walk</u>, **and** <u>skip</u>.

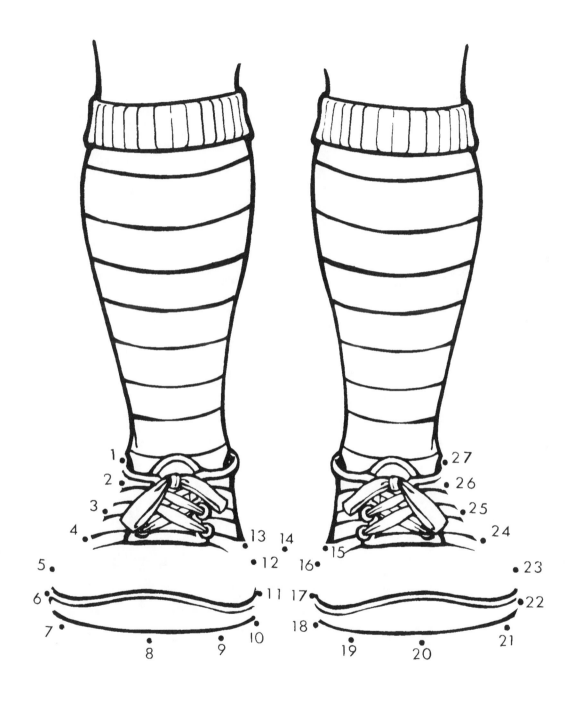

Color the picture.

Teacher check _____

Initial   Date

Name _____

Draw a picture of yourself exercising.

Teacher check _____

Initial   Date

Name _____

My Sit-up Chart

Day	Number of Sit-ups	Day	Number of Sit-ups

Science 106
Worksheet 15
with page 29

 Teacher check _____

Initial   Date

Name _____

Write the name of the special exercise.

| jumping jacks | pushups |
| sit-ups | toe-touches |

_____

- -

_____

_____

- -

_____

_____

- -

_____

_____

- -

Color the pictures.

_____

Teacher check _____

Initial   Date

Name _____

Make a mobile to hang in your room.

You need:

crayons
scissors
glue
3 sticks or a coat hanger

colored paper or
cardboard
string

Color the pictures on Worksheet 18.

Cut out the pieces on Worksheet 18.

Glue them to paper or cardboard.

Put string through the holes.

Tie string to sticks or coat hanger.

Hang it in your room.

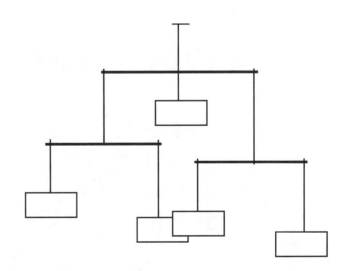

 Teacher check _____
Initial   Date

Name _____

BUILDING A BETTER BODY

GOOD FOOD

ENOUGH SLEEP

EXERCISE

Science 106
Worksheet 18
with page 33

Teacher check _____

Initial   Date

248

Name _____

Complete each sentence.

_____

I live in _____ .

your state

_____

My state is in the _____ .

region

_____

One animal that lives here is the _____

_____

_____ .

_____

A plant that grows here is the _____

_____

_____ .

Science: 107
Worksheet 1
with page 3

 Teacher check _____

Initial   Date

249

Name _____

Follow the dots to see another woodland animal.

I am a _____ .

Teacher check _____

Initial   Date

250

Color the cactus.

saguaro

barrel

prickly pear

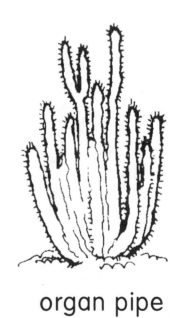

organ pipe

Science: 107
Worksheet 3
with page 7

 Teacher check _____

Initial   Date

Name _____

Some people like to live in the desert.

The desert is sunny and warm.

Farmers can grow crops all year.

Color the pictures.
Write a sentence about the desert in your Tablet.

Science: 107
Worksheet 4
with page 7

Teacher check _____

Initial   Date

252

Name _____

Follow the dots to find another animal of the grassland.

I am a _____ .

Teacher check _____

Initial   Date

Name _____

Section I: Review

Color the pictures. Write the word.

mountains	grasslands
woodlands	desert

_____

- - - - - - - - - - - - -

_____

_____

- - - - - - - - - - - - -

_____

Science: 107
Worksheet 6
with page 12

Teacher check _____

Initial   Date

254

Name _____

Help each animal find its way home.

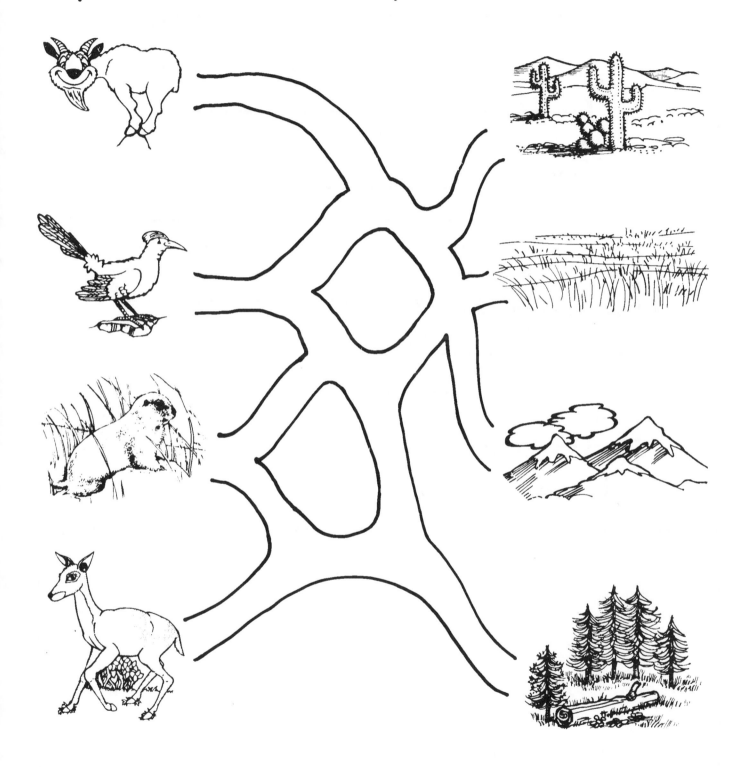

Science: 107
Worksheet 7
with page 15

Teacher check _____

Initial   Date

255

Name _____

Write the words.

dolphin	ocean
gills	salty

_____

Ocean water is_____ .

_____

Dazy is a _____ .

_____

Fish have _____ .

_____

An_____ is very big.

Draw a picture of a fish.

Science: 107
Worksheet 8
with page 18

Teacher check _____
Initial   Date

256

Name _____

Fun at the Seashore
- a picture to color -

Science: 107
Worksheet 9
with page 21

 Teacher check _____

Initial   Date

257

Name _____

Fun at the Lake.

Follow the dots. Color the picture.

Teacher check _____

Initial   Date

Name _____

Color the riverboat.

 Teacher check _____

Initial   Date

Name _____

Section 2: Review

Help the animal find its home.

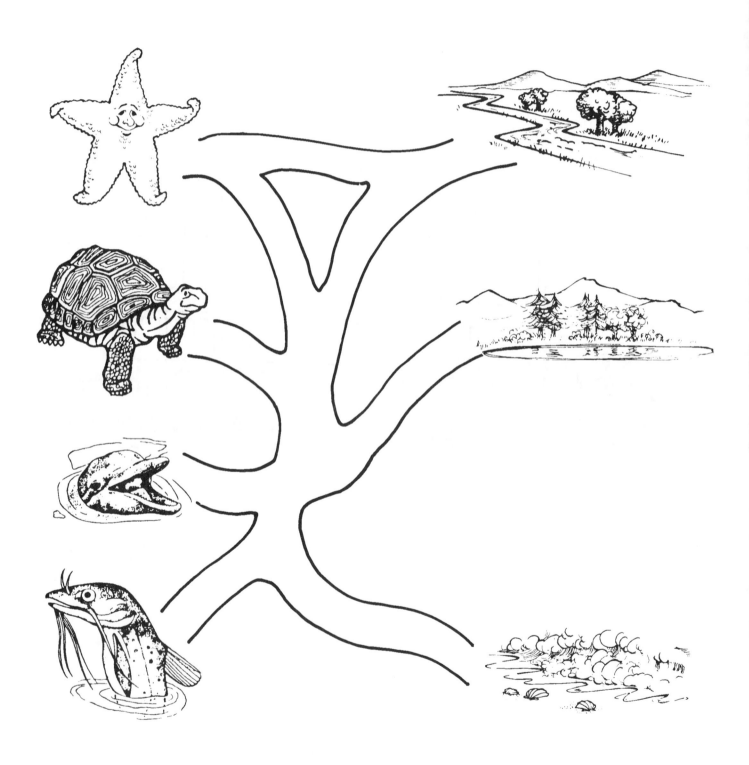

 Teacher check _____

Initial   Date

260

Name _____

Make compound words.
Match the words.
Write the compound word.

rain   fish   raindrop

sun   drop

star   land

grass   shine

---

road   land

wood   fish

sea   runner

cat   shore

Science: 107
Worksheet 13
with page 31

Teacher check _____

Initial   Date

261

Name _____

Color the things in the picture that show the wind is blowing.

Circle <u>yes</u> **or** <u>no</u>.

The wind can move things.

yes / no

You can see the wind.

yes / no

Science: 107
Worksheet 14
with page 35

Teacher check _____

Initial   Date

262

Make a summer tree or a fall tree.

Take colored paper (green for summer, or orange, yellow, red for fall).

Cut out small leaves.

Paste them to the tree.

Color the other parts of the picture.

Color the sky.

Write summer or fall. _____

Teacher check _____

Initial   Date

Name _____

A Beautiful Day

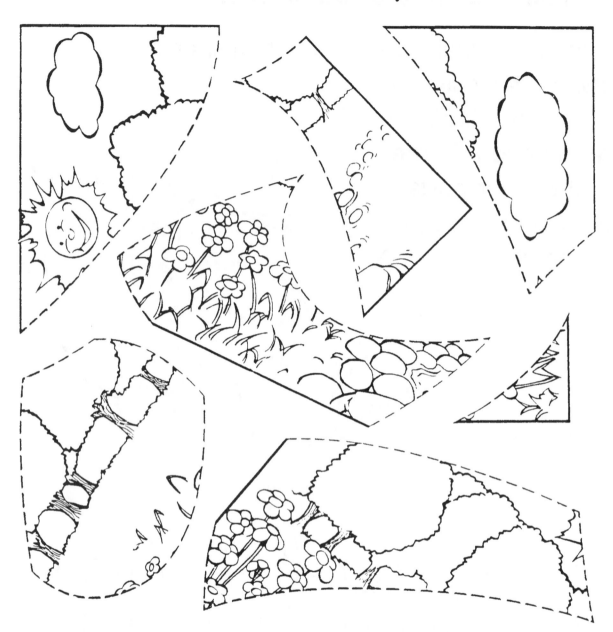

Directions: Color the picture.
             Paste it on cardboard.
             Cut on the lines.
             Put your puzzle together.
             Store the pieces in an
             envelope.

Teacher check _____

                                            Initial   Date

Name _____

Color the picture.

Read the sentence.

Sunny can <u>see</u> the light.

Sunny can <u>feel</u> the heat.

Science: 108
Worksheet 1
with page 4

 Teacher check _____

Initial   Date

265

Name _____

Find two ways energy gets to you.

 Teacher check _____

Initial   Date

266

Name _____

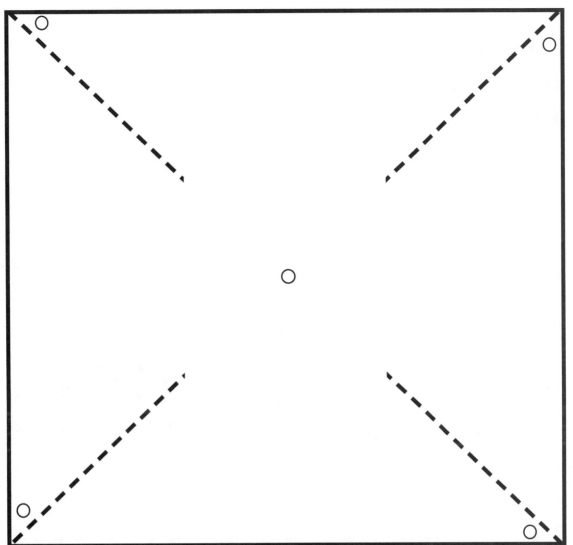

Make the wind work.
Directions

1. Cut out the pinwheel.

2. Color it on both sides.

3. Ask your teacher to help you
   pin your wheel to a stick.

4. It should look like the picture.

Teacher check _____

Initial   Date

Name _____

Color the pictures.

Cut them apart.

Put them in order.

Glue them onto Worksheet 5.

Teacher check _____

Initial   Date

Name _____

The Big Wind Did it

1.	2.
3.	4.

Science: 108
Worksheet 5
with page 11

 Teacher check _____

Initial   Date

269

Name _____

Draw the raindrop.
Draw a place it might land the next time it comes.

Science: 108
Worksheet 6
with page 15

Teacher check _____
Initial   Date

270

Name _____

Draw a picture for each energy word.

sun	plants
wind	animals
water	you

Science: 108
Worksheet 7
with page 18

Teacher check _____
Initial   Date

271

Name _____

This animal does hard work.
Follow the dots to see. Color the picture.

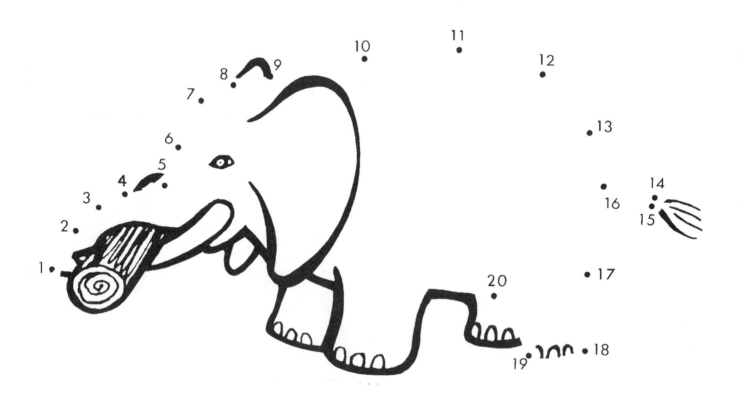

Teacher check _____

Initial   Date

Name _____

Circle the place each fuel is found.

coal

wood

oil

gasoline

Science: 108
Worksheet 9
with page 23

 Teacher check _____

Initial   Date

273

Name _____

Color Benjamin Franklin and his kite.

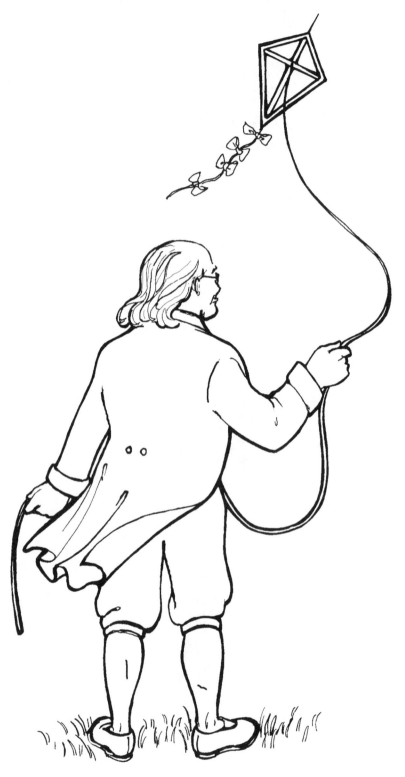

 Teacher check _____

Initial   Date

Name _____

Color the pictures.

Cut on the dotted lines.

Glue them on Worksheet 12.

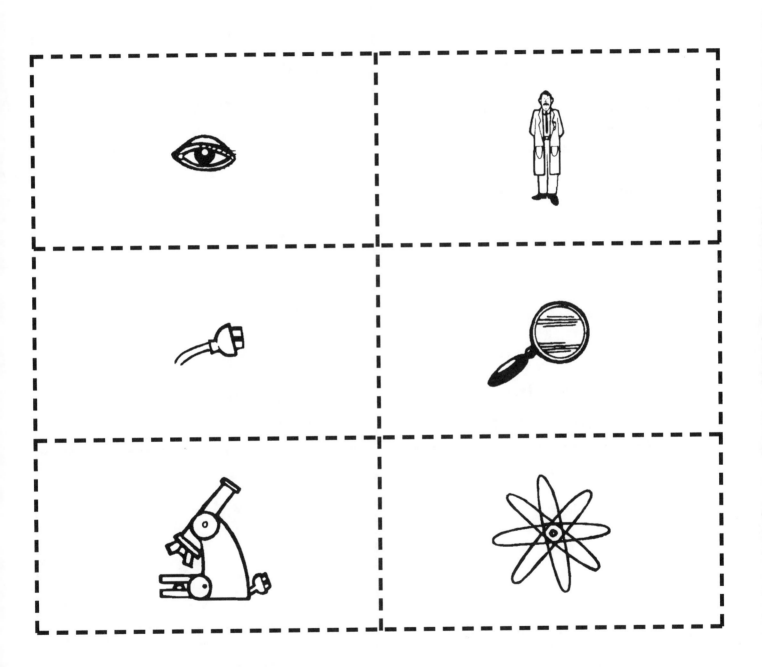

Science: 108
Worksheet 11
with page 31

 Teacher check _____

Initial   Date

275

Scientists looked for answers.

They looked with their **eyes**.

They looked with a **magnifying glass.**

They looked with a **microscope.**

Scientists learned about **atoms.**

Nuclear energy can make **electricity.**

 Teacher check _____

Initial   Date

Draw energy God gives us.

Draw energy we use.

Science: 108
Worksheet 13
with page 33

Teacher check _____

Initial   Date

277

When the sun has gone to bed
It's, oh, so dark at night.
When you have to read or write,
Of course, you need some light.
but, when it's getting very late
and time to go to bed,
Please turn me off!
Don't leave me on!
Save energy, instead!

Follow the dots to see what to turn off to save energy.

Science: 108
Worksheet 14
with page 35

Teacher check _____

Initial   Date

278

Draw a lever to do each job.

Science: 109
Worksheet 1
with page 7

 Teacher check _____
Initial   Date

279

Name _____

Circle the tools made of levers.
Color the picture.

Science: 109
Worksheet 2
with page 9

Teacher check _____

Initial   Date

280

Name _____

A wheelbarrow is a lever.

Color the wheelbarrow.

load

fulcrum

force

Discuss the position of the fulcrum in front of the load.

Science: 109
Worksheet 3
with page 11

 Teacher check _____

Initial   Date

281

Name _____

Circle the levers.

Teacher check _____

Initial   Date

Name _____

Draw four things with wheels.
Color your pictures.

Science: 109
Worksheet 5
with page 17

Teacher check _____

Initial   Date

283

Draw a third gear to make the other gears turn.

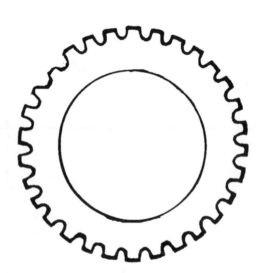

 Teacher check _____

Initial   Date

Circle the pulleys.
Color the picture.

Teacher check _____

Initial   Date

Write <u>L</u> on the levers.
Write <u>W</u> on the wheels.

Teacher check _____

Initial   Date

Name _____

The boy wants to take his wagon over the log.
Draw <u>inclined planes</u> **that will help.**

Teacher check _____

Initial   Date

Name _____

Finish the pictures.
Draw inclined planes.

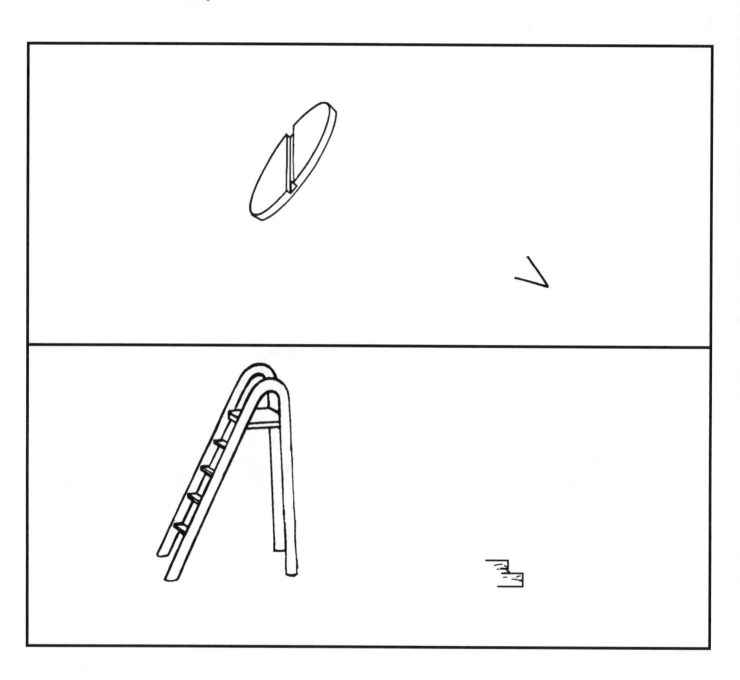

Science: 109
Worksheet 10
with page 29

Teacher check _____

 Initial   Date

288

Name _____

Write <u>lever</u>, <u>wheel</u>, **or** <u>inclined plane</u>.

_____
- -
_____

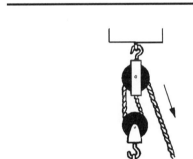   

_____
- -
_____

_____
- -
_____

Science: 109
Worksheet 11
with page 33

 Teacher check _____
                                    Initial   Date

289

Name _____

Write the words to name each sense.

sight	hearing	touch	taste	smell

_____

- -

_____

_____

- -

_____

_____

- -

_____

_____

- -

_____

_____

- -

_____

Science: 110
Worksheet 1
with page 2

 Teacher check _____

Initial   Date

291

Match each shape to its name.

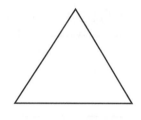

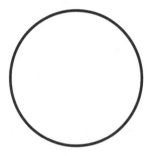

rectangle

square

triangle

circle

Color the rectangle <u>green</u>.
Color the triangle <u>yellow</u>.
Color the circle <u>blue</u>.
Color the square <u>red</u>.

 Teacher check _____

Name _____

Color the pictures to match the sentences.

The dog is brown.
The shirt is orange.
The sun is yellow.
The cat is black.
The tree is green.
The dress is purple.
The flag is red, white, and blue.

Science: 110
Worksheet 3
with page 5

 Teacher check _____
Initial   Date

293

Name _____

Circle sounds of nature. Color the pictures.

 Teacher check _____

Initial   Date

Name _____

Circle the noisy things. Color the pictures.

Too much noise is
sound pollution.

 Teacher check _____

Initial   Date

295

Which sense do you use?

Write T **for taste.**

Write S **for smell.**

Write TS **if you can taste and smell.**

_____
- - - - - - - - - - - - - - - - - - - -
_____

_____
- - - - - - - - - - - - - - - - - - - -
_____

_____
- - - - - - - - - - - - - - - - - - - -
_____

_____
- - - - - - - - - - - - - - - - - - - -
_____

Science 110
Worksheet 6
with page 9

 Teacher check _____

Initial   Date

296

Make a FEELY BOX.

You need:

shoebox	tape
scissors	some things to feel

What to do.

1. Cut a hole in one end of the box.

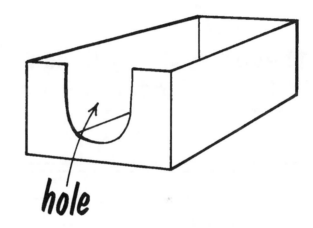

hole

2. Tape the cover on the box.

3. Put something in the box. Ask a friend to guess what it is by feeling.

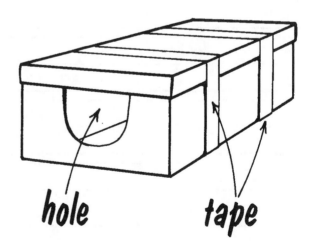

hole   *tape*

Science: 110
Worksheet 7
with page 11

 Teacher check _____
Initial   Date

297

Name _____

These are living things.
Write each name where it belongs.

Plants	Animals

Science: 110
Worksheet 8
with page 16

Teacher check _____
Initial   Date

298

Think of a machine to help you work.
Draw a picture of your machine.
Tell what it does.

My machine is a _____ .

It can _____ .

Science: 110
Worksheet 9
with page 18

Teacher check _____
Initial   Date

299

Name _____

Some things change in many ways.

A butterfly lays her eggs.

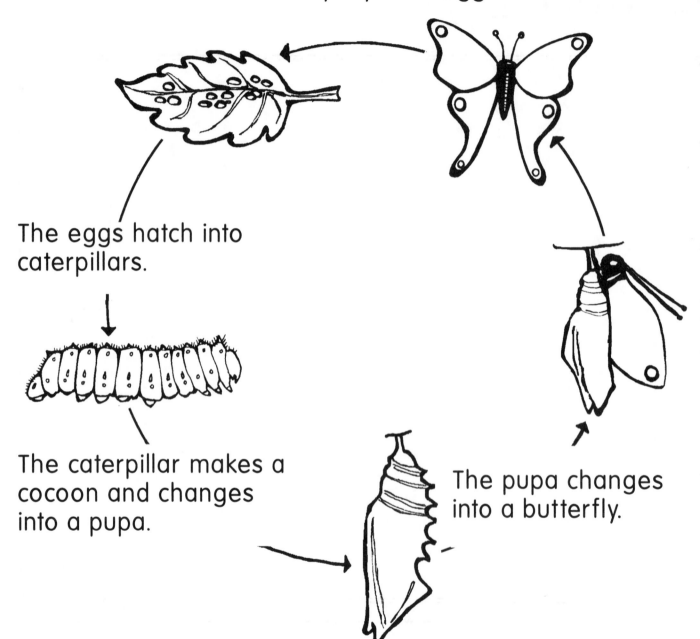

The eggs hatch into caterpillars.

The caterpillar makes a cocoon and changes into a pupa.

The pupa changes into a butterfly.

Read and discuss.
Color the pictures.

Science: 110
Worksheet 10
with page 21

Teacher check _____

Initial   Date

300

Name _____

Draw a picture of your favorite weather.

Science: 110
Worksheet 11
with page 22

Teacher check _____

Initial   Date

301

Name _____

Match the words to the pictures.

exercise

good food

enough sleep

keeping clean

Science: 110
Worksheet 12
with page 27

Teacher check _____

Initial   Date

302

Name _____

These children are making a pretty garden.

Color the picture.

Science: 110
Worksheet 13
with page 29

Teacher check _____

Initial   Date

303

Name _____

Follow the dots to see what saves energy.
Start with A. Color your picture.

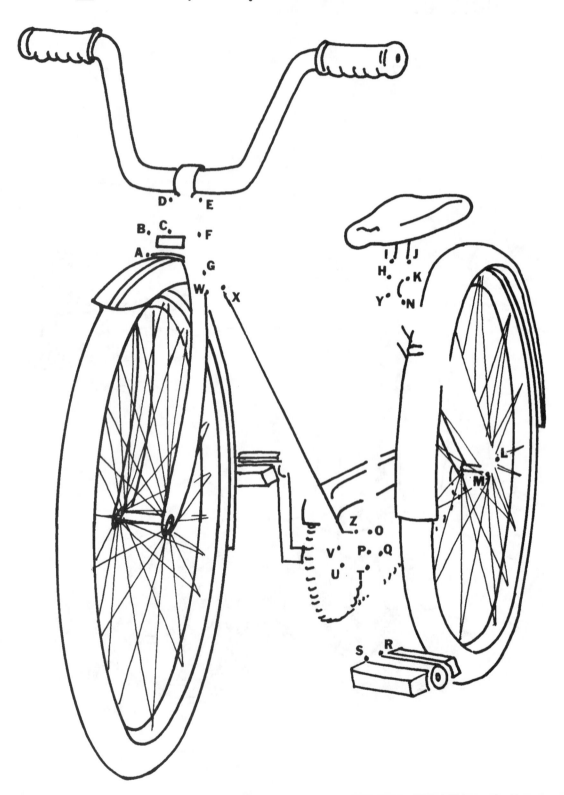

Science: 110
Worksheet 14
with page 30

Teacher check _____

Initial   Date

304

Name _____

Write ways that you can help save energy.
Ask your teacher to help.

_____

_____

_____

_____

_____

_____

_____

_____

_____

_____

_____

_____

_____

_____

Science: 110
Worksheet 15
with page 30

Teacher check _____

Name _____

Make a change collage.

1. **Color the picture.**
2. **Cut it out.**
2. **Paste it on a big sheet of paper.**
3. **Cut out or draw pictures of other changes you have studied.**

Science: 110
Worksheet 16
with page 33

Teacher check _____

Initial   Date

ALTERNATE

T
E
S
T
S

Reproducible Tests
for use with the Science 100
Teacher's Guide

SCIENCE

1 0 6

ALTERNATE
LIFEPAC TEST

14/17

Name_____

Date_____

Score_____

SCIENCE 106: ALTERNATE LIFEPAC TEST

Circle the things that can grow.

Write the answer.

man	cat	plant

Dan will grow to be a _____ .

Tat will grow to be a _____ .

A seed will grow to be a _____ .

Draw ☺ **or** ☹ .

Circle the answer.

How many hours should you sleep?

2   5   8   10

Circle the good foods.

Write the words.

exercise   muscles

Running and jumping are good
_____

_____ .

_____

Exercise keeps your _____ healthy.

NOTES

SCIENCE

1 0 7

ALTERNATE
LIFEPAC TEST

10/13

Name _____

Date _____

Score _____

SCIENCE 107: ALTERNATE LIFEPAC TEST

Write the answer.

Snow and sunshine are kinds of _____ .
weather   seasons

Each year has _____ seasons.
two   four

You find water in_____ .
oceans   deserts

Deserts are very _____ .
dry   wet

page 1 (one)

Name the seasons.

spring	autumn	summer	winter

Match the animal to its home.

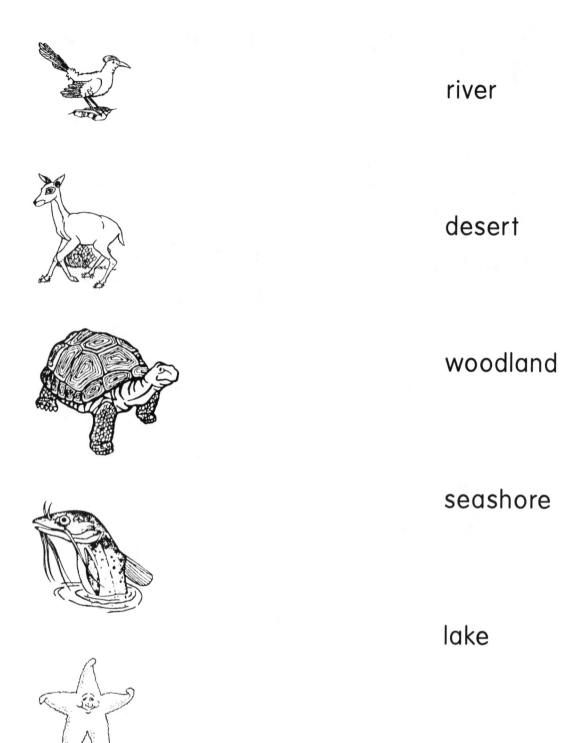

river

desert

woodland

seashore

lake

SCIENCE

108

ALTERNATE LIFEPAC TEST

10 / 13

Name _____

Date _____

Score _____

SCIENCE 108: ALTERNATE LIFEPAC TEST

Circle the word.

Food is _____.
fuel / energy

Wind is moving _____.
water / air

You should _____ energy.
save / waste

Using the _____ energy saves fuel.
sun / sun's

Sun energy is called _____.
solar / water

God made _____ energy.
nuclear / solar

Circle <u>fact</u> **or** <u>fantasy</u>.

Scientists can split atoms.   fact / fantasy

Cows can fly.   fact / fantasy

Match the picture with the fuel.

Draw two ways you can help save energy.

SCIENCE

1 0 9

ALTERNATE
LIFEPAC TEST

10 / 12

Name _____

Date _____

Score _____

SCIENCE 109: ALTERNATE LIFEPAC TEST

Write the words.

move	ramp	simple machines
gear	levers	pulley

A wheel with teeth is a _____ .

A wheel with rope is a _____ .

Scissors are two _____ .

A _____ is an inclined plane.

Wheels and levers help things _____ .

Wheels, levers, and inclined planes are _____ _____ .

Match the words to the pictures.

wheel

lever

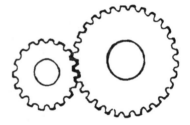

inclined plane

NOTES

page 3 (three)

NOTES

SCIENCE

110

ALTERNATE LIFEPAC TEST

12 / 14

Name _____

Date _____

Score _____

SCIENCE 110: ALTERNATE LIFEPAC TEST

Draw a line to match.

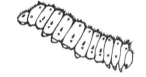

Circle <u>yes</u> or <u>no</u>.

Food gives you energy.	yes	no
I use my head to observe.	yes	no
Riding a bike wastes energy.	yes	no
Simple machines make work easier.	yes	no

page 1 (one)